Rocks, Minerals & Gemstones

Rocks, Minerals & Gemstones

I. O. Evans

Hamlyn
London·New York·Sydney·Toronto

Published by
THE HAMLYN PUBLISHING GROUP LIMITED
London · New York · Sydney · Toronto
Hamlyn House, Feltham, Middlesex, England
Copyright © The Hamlyn Publishing Group Limited 1972

ISBN 0 600 37537 4

Printed in Spain
By Printer, Industria Grafica S.A. Tuset 19
Barcelona, San Vicente Dels Horts 1972
Deposito Legal B. 24-193-1972
Mohn Gordon Ltd. London

Contents

The Earth – past and present

Flint implement from the early Old Stone Age when flints were chipped into shape.

Although man has always obtained his food and garments from animals and plants, he has gained his shelter, his tools and weapons, and many of the amenities of his life, from the rocks and their mineral contents. Windbreaks and rock shelters gave way to houses, decorated caves to art galleries and temples, and flint was superseded as the chief raw material by copper, bronze, iron, steel and a host of other metals and alloys. Precious metals and gemstones used for personal adornment, and later as symbols of wealth, probably attracted attention even before copper. The rocks also became the great source of water, first in springs and streams and later reached by wells and pumps, thus deciding the position of centres of human habitation.

As man increased in numbers and human needs grew, precious and useful metals alike had to be won by quarrying and mining, too often by slave or sweated labour. The passage quoted from the New English Bible paints a vivid picture of the miners' toils, hardships and triumphs (Job 28: 1–11).

'There are mines for silver and places where men refine gold; where iron is won from the earth and copper smelted from the ore; the end of the seam lies in darkness, and it is followed to its farthest limit. Strangers cut the galleries; they are forgotten as they drive forward far from men. While corn is springing from the earth above, what lies beneath is raked over like a fire, and out of its rocks comes lapis lazuli, dusted with flecks of gold. No bird of prey knows the way there, and the falcon's keen eye cannot descry it; proud beasts do not set foot on it, and no serpent comes that way. Man sets his hand to the granite rock and lays bare the roots of the mountains; he cuts galleries in the rocks, and gems of every kind meet his eye; he dams up the sources of the streams and brings the hidden riches of the earth to light.'

The quest for metal stimulated travel and exploration leading to foreign conquest and the establishment of trade routes: even before the Christian era the Phoenicians conveyed metal and other commodities about the Mediterranean and imported tin from Cornwall. The use of power-driven machinery made civilization even more dependent on materials won from the rocks, and this machinery was developed as a result of the growing difficulties which the work involved. Indeed, the steam engine itself was produced in response not to any demand for improved methods of transport by land or sea, but to the increased demands being made for coal and metallic ores just as the more accessible coal seams and veins of Cornish tin were being exhausted.

As the mines were dug more deeply the labour of working them and keeping them clear of flood water grew more and more difficult. The early Newcomen steam engine could not cope with the task of pumping, and it was not until it was perfected by James Watt in 1763 that this was accomplished. Steam power was soon adapted for land and sea transport, for hauling up loads of coal and ore from the mines, and for use in factories, and thus mankind reached a new stage in history, the present Machine Age. In Britain, where the coal and iron mines lay side by side, the steam engine was put into mass production and from Britain, for a time the 'workshop of the world', railways and steamship routes spread about the Earth.

About a century ago petrol began to supplant coal as a source of power and as mastery of the new inventions spread every nation

became its own workshop. Air power began to supplant naval power and electricity to supplant steam. In the present century radioactivity has been discovered. Its use in the atomic and hydrogen bombs rendered warfare more horrible, but efforts are now being made to harness the energy locked within the atom for the service of man.

The study of rocks and minerals did not become a science, geology, until the nineteenth century. Man has always been interested in nature and anxious to know the world's history, and the practical tasks of winning and working flint and metal led to the accumulation of theoretical knowledge. In spite of the attempts made by miners and alchemists to guard their trade secrets, the foundations of Earth-lore were laid.

Apart from its practical use, geology has now become an important branch of science and is receiving increasing attention from educationalists, and while offering the prospect of a splendid career it is fascinating for its own sake. It has transformed our religious outlook, providing evidence both for the Earth's antiquity and, from the fossils, for the evolution of living beings from a lowly ancestry to the plants and animals of today – and to ourselves.

The manufacture of flint implements in the New Stone Age when they were not only chipped but polished. Polishing of flints as distinct from their chipping seems to have been associated with the development of cultivation.

The origin of the Earth is a matter for consideration by the astronomer, that of life a matter for the biologist. The work of the geologist begins with the formation of solid rocks but that of the palaeontologist, the student of the extinct forms of life, from the period when living creatures first left recognizable remains. Knowledge of the general development of fossil forms is essential for the study of rocks and minerals, for it throws light on the succession of the rock beds and this has important practical applications.

The most accurate method of dating the beds utilizes the radioactive decay of certain minerals, uranium, for example, breaking down at a known rate into a form of lead. The succession of the rock beds is also shown by the order in which they occur: when one bed rests upon another, then, unless their position has later been altered, the lowermost of the two is the older. A rough-and-ready guide to the comparative age of similar beds is also given by their hardness.

The five great Eras into which the rocks are classified may well be considered here. What were once regarded as the very oldest rocks were called Cambrian and so others, far older, which were later discovered in the Canadian Shield east of the Rocky Mountains and in the Highlands of Scotland, are classed as Precambrian;

These rock beds show how strata originally deposited horizontally can be tipped to slope steeply by earth movements.

the earliest of these may be 3,000 million years old. They are very hard and abound in mineral wealth but contain very few fossils; those found in the more recent of these beds are of invertebrates and lack the hard parts – bones, shells and so forth – most likely to be preserved.

Fossils, at first solely of marine creatures, first became plentiful in the Cambrian beds (formed about 500 million years ago) which open the Palaeozoic Era, the Age of Ancient Life. Lowly animals were followed by fishes and then life spread to the land with the amphibians and insects; the forests forming the Coal Measures also belong to this Era.

The Mesozoic Era, the Age of Middle Life, dates from about 200 million years ago and it includes the appearance of giant reptiles. The earliest birds and mammals appeared in its later stages during which the chalk was formed and many trees were of modern type.

The Cainozoic Era, the Age of Recent Life, started about sixty million years ago. It comprises the Tertiary Period, the Age of Mammals, in which the animals increasingly resembled those of to-day, and the Quaternary Period, the Age of Man, which brings the record of the rocks up to our own time. The Great Ice Age also belongs to this Era.

A steep-sided canyon cut in hard rock beds: the Aare Schlucht near Meringen, Switzerland.

The Horse Shoe Falls on the Canadian side of Niagara where the river has excavated a deep gorge between 6 and 7 miles long and is slowly cutting its way upstream.

It was William Smith, the Father of English Geology, who first observed that each zone or layer of rocks in a rock bed has its own typical fossils not found elsewhere. The relative age or position in the time sequence of a zone could therefore be calculated from its distinctive fossils and this knowledge is essential to prospectors and mining engineers. Thus, when the British geologist Sir George Lyell visited America he was able to deduce from surface indications that the rocks in one state were worth working for coal, whereas those of another were not.

Right from their formation the rocks are attacked and shattered by the weather. Their fragments consolidate on the sea floor and are later raised by earth movements to become new beds of rock. The rocks thus formed are called sedimentary. Volumes of molten material have from time to time forced their way up from within the Earth and cooled to form a very different type of rock, the igneous rocks. These are rich in minerals but as one would expect from their origin, they are almost devoid of fossils. The heat from such up-rushes of molten material and the pressure produced by powerful earth movements have so modified the structure of certain beds as to produce yet another type, the metamorphic rocks. Each of these rock types will be considered in more detail in the following chapters.

Differences in the hardness and texture of the rocks, and hence in their resistance to the weather, naturally have their effects on the scenery. The many kinds of rock found in Britain produce the great diversity of its landscape, whereas wide stretches of similar rocks underlie the American prairies and the Russian steppes. The hardest rocks form the core of great mountain ranges with their rugged crests and precipitous slopes; the less resistant produce rounded hills and very soft rocks form the lowlands. The folding of the rock beds can also produce marked scenic effects, as may the faults or cracks which split them.

The tiny particles produced from the rocks by weathering are converted into soil by the action and decomposition of plants and animals. Each kind of rock forms a typical soil and this affects its

Opposite The Bryce Canyon in Utah, USA, shows the stratification of the rocks and the action of the wind in cutting them into fantastically shaped pinnacles.

A drowned valley where the land has
subsided and the sea has come flooding
in. The silt bordering the stream has
been brought down by the river and
illustrates the destructive effect of water
on the land.

The limestone pavement at the head of
Malham Cove, Yorkshire, England,
resembling the Karst of Yugoslavia.
This formation, in which the rock is
trenched with deep furrows, is
characteristic of limestone and is caused
by the action of the rain.

plant and animal life and may decide its suitability for cultivation.

Rainfall accumulates in streams and rivers and these both destroy much of the land and extend its area. In the head-waters where the movement is most violent, the water and the material it carries scour away the bed; further down it deposits roughly as much material as it erodes, and near the mouth some of this material accumulates beside its course. The river cuts hard rocks downwards forming steep-sided gorges: the Grand Canyon of the Colorado River is a stupendous example. In softer country it cuts sideways, producing a broad open valley with gently sloping sides. Where hard rocks lie downstream from the soft, the valley narrows and the water speeds up. Where the softer rocks lie downstream the river may produce a waterfall, slowly cutting its way backwards to form a gorge like that below Niagara.

The silt brought down by a river may choke the lakes along its course and produce broad plains bordering its mouth, like the Low Countries beside that of the Rhine. Most of the material carried down by the rivers is, however, swept out to sea, destroying the land piecemeal. The great Mississippi sweeps down over 400 million tons of material every year from its basin and is lowering the area at the average rate of one foot in about 3,000 years, even though its delta is advancing by about a mile every sixteen years. Land has also

Naeroysdal Gorge in Norway is formed in hard rocks by the action of water. Weathering has reduced the steepness of the rock and produced a number of screes where the hillside meets the valley.

Opposite Granite rocks are not stratified but are traversed by joints caused by contraction in cooling. This produces the appearance of masonry and is known as mural jointing. Even these rocks, however, are rounded by the action of the waves at sea level.

Some contrasts in limestone scenery. Left Stalactites in the Grotte di Castellana, Puglia, Italy. Below The Minerva Springs in the Yellowstone Park, Wyoming, USA. The material covering the rocks is formed by precipitation from streams.

been destroyed by moving ice, for the polar ice cap extended far south into Eurasia and North America. This Great Ice Age, which ended about 20,000 years ago, produced remarkable effects on the scenery.

Much rain seeps into porous rocks and accumulates undergound, flowing out in springs or being easily accessible near the junction of these rocks with such non-porous beds as clays, and thus facilitating human settlement. The rain forms a weak solution of carbonic acid from the carbon dioxide in the air and dissolves limestone, forming vertical swallow-holes and caves. Some of these become enormous and the Mammoth Cave of Kentucky, for example, has over thirty miles of continuous tunnels. Deposited as dripstone within the caves, the calcium carbonate dissolved in the water forms a strange subterranean scenery of stalactites hanging from the cave roof, stalagmites rising from the floor and stone pillars extending from floor to roof.

Soft rocks along the coast are quickly destroyed by waves, whereas hard rocks resist its attacks; where the two alternate a varied shoreline of bays and creeks and stretches of cliff and headlands is formed. Some of the material thus eroded is swept along by the tides and accumulates to form sandy and pebble beaches. New stretches of land may be produced, later to be cultivated and built upon while seaports may be cut off from the coast. On the whole, however, the action of the sea, like that of the rivers, is destructive, wearing away the edges of the land.

The igneous rocks, consisting mostly of very hard material, can produce striking scenic effects. Steep conical hills may grow around the vents of former volcanoes; prominent ridges and picturesque prism-shaped rocks can be built by basalt; and tors resembling gigantic works of masonry are produced by granite. The great lava flows of Iceland seem literally out of this world and resemble part of the surface of the moon.

The erosive wave action can produce an unusual honeycombing effect in some rocks.

In a chalk coastline the waves tunnel shallow sea-caves into the cliffs but the rock is so soft that their roofs soon collapse forming a coast of inlets separated by headlands.

Opposite Granite in Dartmoor, England, is weathered into characteristic shapes which form a feature of this area.

Sedimentary rocks

The grains in sandstone have been smoothed and polished by the action of the wind and then cemented together to form a solid rock.

To the geologist any considerable mass of material that forms part of the Earth's solid body, irrespective of its hardness or firmness, is a rock, a stretch of clay or a peat bog as much as granite or marble. So also is loess, an accumulation of wind-blown dust found in the large river valleys of America and Europe and especially in China, where cave-dwellings have been dug into it: this is classed for convenience among the sedimentary rocks. A rock may be formed of only one mineral or of several, a mineral almost always having a definite chemical composition.

The eighteenth-century German mineralogist Abraham Werner held that almost all the rocks were produced either as a sort of sludge or as a sediment on the floor of an immense ocean which had once covered the whole Earth. Even when such extravagant ideas were dispelled the nature of many of them was still obvious.

Sandstone, for example, plainly consists of grains of sand, lying in parallel layers and welded into a more or less solid mass by a natural cement. Leonardo da Vinci was one of the earliest thinkers to realize this, and it was demonstrated in the laboratory by the first experimental geologist, Sir James Hall, towards the end of the eighteenth century. Heating sand for some time at the bottom of a cauldron filled with sea water, and replenishing this as it boiled away, he found that the sand solidified. What he had achieved so quickly by the aid of heat he realized might well be accomplished by natural forces acting at ordinary temperatures for an immensely long period.

The sand itself is, technically speaking, a rock. Its nature was long in doubt and it was even thought for a time that, like salt, it was naturally formed by the sea. It really consists of fragments worn from the rocks by weathering and transported, perhaps over long distances, by wind or water and accumulated where the action of these was checked; the neighbouring grains are more or less the same size. Examination under the microscope shows that grains of wind-blown sand are smooth and round but those that are water-borne are more irregular and rough: the wind-blown grains are swirled against one another repeatedly in the air whereas in water the force of their impact is cushioned.

The sand, and the sandstone into which it hardens, is formed of grains of the older rocks, their most common constituent being quartz. Grains of mica give the sand and the sandstone a characteristic glitter, and as the flat flakes usually have faces parallel to the bedding of the rock, they make this micaceous sandstone easy to split into thin slabs. Sand and sandstone may also contain small quantities of such minerals as tourmaline, garnet, magnetite –

Ripple marks in sandstone are produced by the action of the wind and waves on some early beach.

False bedding in sandstone is produced by the action of currents in the water from which the sand was deposited.

which can at once be identified and extracted with a magnet – and green glauconite.

Grains of feldspar are comparatively rare, for this mineral speedily breaks down into clay under the action of the weather. These grains, like those of quartz and mica, come from the granite, and if the feldspar is present in any quantity, it shows that the granite was too short a distance away for its complete disintegration to take place. Such a feldspathic sandstone is also known as an arkose.

Stretches of sand and similar rocks are almost barren and the grains are readily blown along, perhaps with disastrous results to the cultivated or built-on regions in their lee unless they can be bound and rendered fertile by such hardy plants as marram grass. Deserts consist of arid tracts of loose sand and sandstone where water is either entirely absent or lies inaccessibly beneath the surface. Many deserts may be the result, like the dust bowl formed in America some years ago, of injudicious farming. Fortunately they can be reclaimed by irrigation, by the planting of suitable trees or the tapping of underground waters. Sandstone scenery usually consists of moorland and pinewoods, ill-adapted to cultivation but with a dry porous soil.

The sand revealed in a dune which has been cut open may show a rough arrangement into layers; this stratification is much more regular in the sandstones, and in these rocks layers of coarse sand, fine sand and sandy clay may alternate. Damp sand takes the imprint of whatever crosses or touches it, and although such marks are usually effaced by the wind, some may survive as the sand hardens. Thus a layer of sandstone may still bear the trails of marine creatures or the tracks of birds or other animals left when the rock was still a beach washed by some long-vanished sea. Sandstone may also be marked with rain-prints or with the ripples formed by air currents or by waves in shallow water.

The layers of the sandstone are those in which the sand was originally deposited on a level or gently sloping sea floor. In some of these rocks, however, the layers are arranged diagonally in contrasting directions. This current bedding or false bedding is attributed to changes in the direction of the currents in the water where it was formed, much as slag tipped from trucks on a pit bank accumulates in oblique layers at its end.

Where the grains in a sandstone are larger or rougher than usual the rock is called a grit; Millstone Grit is associated with the Coal Measures of Britain and its name is derived from its traditional use. A nondescript sort of dark rock, formed of coarse grains of quartz and other minerals and perhaps containing large flakes of such rocks as slate, is rather vaguely known as a greywacke. This term, of German origin, was once used for any rock which defied more precise classification. Quartzite may be either a very hard tough sandstone which has been cemented so completely by a siliceous cement that its grains break as readily as the cement itself, or a sandstone which has become transformed by heat and pressure.

The commonest cement in these rocks comes from calcite, from a clayey material or from iron ore. The colour of the rock depends partly on that of the grains, partly on that of the cement. Iron oxide, which may form a layer around the grains, can tint the rock yellow, brown or red; the dark hue of the Old Red Sandstone, characteristic of Scotland and South Wales and elsewhere in northern Europe and America, contrasts with the lighter tint of the New Red

Sandstone of south Devon and of the Bunter (brightly coloured) Sandstone of Germany. Some of the coloured sandstones are very attractively mottled.

Different kinds of rock are apt to grade imperceptibly into one another making it impossible to decide just where a very coarse sand becomes a gravel, where a gravel becomes pebbles or a shingle, or where a pebble becomes a rounded boulder. The origin of pebbles was still in dispute when in 1803 the Swiss geologist de Saussure showed that they were fragments of rock transported to their present position by water – later it was seen that some, those on mountain sides, for example, were carried there by glaciers during the Great Ice Age – and rounded and smoothed during the process. Pebbles thus represent a stage through which rock fragments pass before they become sand.

Pebbles are large enough to show the type of rock from which they come and, unlike sand grains, they may consist not of separate minerals but of fragments of the composite rock itself. Thus a granite is not sorted out into quartz, feldspar and mica and a granite pebble may show all three still firmly welded together. All rocks may form pebbles but naturally some are destroyed by the waves more quickly than others. Limestone pebbles may contain fossils either intact or in recognizable fragments.

These pebbles have been rounded by the action of the sea and if the process had continued would have been worn down into grains of sand; or if they were buried by sand would have been cemented into a conglomerate.

The rocks on a cliff are attacked by waves even more fiercely than by the weather so that the pebbles at its base mostly come from the cliff itself. Others have been transported not so much by the currents and tides – they are too massive for this – as by longshore drift, the intermittent movement of the waves along the coast. The waves also sort the pebbles out roughly according to size.

Just as sand is united by a natural cement into sandstone, so the loose pebbles are similarly welded into a conglomerate, also expressively called puddingstone. This rock has a general resemblance to a slice of sandstone as seen under a microscope, except that the proportions between the pebbles or sand grains and the cement are different and the pebbles are more varied. As in the sandstone, the cement in the conglomerate may be one of several different materials, and its hardness decides the firmness of the rock itself. The pebbles in some conglomerates may be picked out with the fingers or may even be so loose that they drop out, but in others they are so completely welded in that, like the grains in quartzite, the rock will break across the pebbles instead of round them – the cement is harder than they are.

The pebbles most commonly found in a conglomerate consist of granite, quartzite, quartz, flint and a very similar material, chert. Limestone pebbles, being much softer, usually occur not in association with these hard rocks but in separate conglomerate formations; basalt, although hard, seldom forms pebbles because when broken into blocks it soon disintegrates. The only ornamental stone in a conglomerate is likely to be jaspar; the only fossils, apart from those in limestone, are those hard enough to survive the pounding of the waves, such as teeth and enamelled fish scales.

The cement in these rocks may consist of calcite, iron oxide or silica, which when hardened is more resistant to breaking than a flint pebble, and fills all the spaces in a bed of shingle. The conglomerate may show bedding but the only indication of this given by the pebbles is that they are roughly graded, the smaller ones being above the larger.

Rock fragments which fall in mountains or out of reach of the waves from cliffs may not be worn into pebbles at all but remain as jagged pieces of stone. However, if they have fallen into still water or are later covered by the sea they may be similarly cemented into a solid mass of rock. This is then called a breccia (an Italian word pronounced to rhyme approximately with stretcher, meaning the rubble from a fallen wall). If these fragments have been affected by water at all they may show signs of this and the rock is then an intermediate between a conglomerate and a breccia. Some of the fragments in a breccia are large enough to be called boulders; some near Gibraltar may weigh twenty or more tons. They may include almost any type of rock, even sun-dried pieces of clay, and among the most common are limestone, sandstone and blocks hurled from volcanoes. The most usual cements are, as in the conglomerates, calcite, silica and iron oxide.

A similar rock consisting entirely of material hurled from volcanoes is called either a volcanic agglomerate if the fragments are sizeable, or a tuff (not to be confused with tufa), if they are not. The tuff is composed of the sand and dust commonly spoken of as volcanic ash which is carried by the wind further from the volcano than the agglomerate; if it is carried out to sea it may mix with the sediment on the sea floor and produce a sandy tuff.

Sand grades down into silt and the sandstone grades down corre-

spondingly into siltstone. The grains, like those of the sandstone, form layers along which the stone readily splits and they are again composed of particles of quartz, feldspar and mica.

The grains of silt grade down still further until they become very fine indeed, less than 0·005 mm in diameter, to form what is sometimes termed rock flour. The minuteness of the grains gives this material properties so distinctive that it deserves a different name: once it has become moist, it is better known as clay.

Most clays, though not all, are plastic but when they are baked either in the sun or artificially, this plasticity is permanently lost. This characteristic has given clay many uses and after flint it has probably been the most valuable mineral, other than the ores, known to man. In the early civilizations of the Middle East it provided writing material and today it provides us with building material as brick. The various minerals in the clay are not easy to identify without the use of an electron microscope but they may include silica, compounds of aluminium, iron oxide and smaller quantities of other minerals; some may have the glint of mica, others the whiteness of kaolin (china clay).

A concretion about 4 inches in diameter. Exposure to the weather has revealed the septaria in the nodule.

When it is dried by the sun but not sufficiently to lose its plasticity, clay becomes very hard, but when damp it softens and regains its plasticity, and rain breaks down its surface into mire which human or animal traffic soon converts into an unpleasant sticky mud. For this reason it is best avoided as building land although it is well suited for certain forms of cultivation. So too are the composite soils which clay helps to form: a mixture of clay and sand produces loam, and marl consists of clay and limestone, but if it contains many limestone fragments it is brashy.

When it extends over a considerable area clay produces a lowland type of scenery and it is readily swept away by streams; when it occurs between two belts of harder rock it forms an inland valley, or on the coast a bay between two headlands. Clay does not show regular stratification but it may be banded into layers less than an inch thick, silty below and clay above. These varves, as they are called, each represent a year's deposit.

Some clays contain concretions formed by the segregating of mineral matter and these range from a few inches to several feet in

diameter. Some concretions are large flints, others consist of iron or calcium carbonate, and some are cracked irregularly from a common centre to near the surface. These cracks gape somewhat and calcite or some other mineral may seep in to fill them. As this material may be more resistant to weathering than the rest of the nodule, the filled-in cracks may stand out somewhat as plates of thin stone; hence the term septarian nodules (from *septum*, the Latin for a plate).

There are several types of clay. Its purest form is china clay or kaolin formed by the disintegration of the feldspar in granite. London Clay, which is represented beyond the Channel by Paris Clay, is bluish below the surface but weathers reddish-brown. Fireclay, which is resistant to very high temperatures, occurs beneath the coal seams of Britain, France and America, having formed the soil in which the coal-producing forests grew.

Clay converted into a solid rock can become either a mudstone which shows no tendency to split into layers but has lost its plasticity, or a shale which splits readily along its bedding planes. If the layers are so thin that they can be turned individually like the pages of a book it is called a paper shale. Oil shales contain so much organic matter that they burn with a smoky flame or can be made to yield quantities of oil. A shale powerfully compressed by earth movements is converted into slate.

Immense masses of clay were formed during the Great Ice Age. As the glaciers travelled southwards the ice smoothed the rocks it moved against, scored them with grooves (glacial striations) with the small fragments of rock wedged into its surface, ploughed them up with larger fragments, ripped away projecting masses from these rocks, and mixed them up with the rock flour which the friction produced. The glaciers spread these masses across the land and drenched them with melt water, and when temperate conditions returned left them covering much of its surface as a sheet of clay with the rock-fragments embedded in it.

This boulder clay, also called glacial clay and till, covers the greater part of Britain as far south as the Thames, almost all Canada and the United States and the northern part of Eurasia. The rocks embedded in the clay, having been sheltered from weathering by the ice, are irregular in shape, the smaller ones being sharply jagged although some of their faces may be grooved or smoothed where they were dragged against the other rocks. When these deposits of till are cemented into a solid body they become tillite.

Smaller deposits of what is known as clay-with-flints were formed on the top of chalk hills after the chalk had been destroyed by weathering, leaving the flints it contained behind. The land, having again subsided below the sea because of further earth movements, became covered with patches of such deposits as the London and Paris Clays to form the clay-with-flints, which is reddish in colour and may be marked by clumps of beech trees growing on the grassy downlands.

Other sedimentary rocks were formed not of silt from the land deposited on the sea floor but by the evaporation of sea water or of the precipitation of the chemicals it contains. Their composition can be mentioned here but they will also be considered later among the minerals.

Among the deposits are several important beds of various types of ironstone. Bacteria may have helped to bring about their precipitation and some of the ironstone is interbedded with such ordinary

A cliff face with well-defined layers of sandstone and shale.

sedimentary rocks as sandstone and shale. The Cleveland Beds of the east of the United States consist of haematite, much of it being oolitic, formed of closely packed coarse grains. The blackband ironstones of America and Europe are impure siderites (iron carbonate); their association with coal seams among the shales makes them valuable economically, but the beds in Luxemburg and Lorraine are composed of limonite (iron oxide).

Rock salt, which consists not only of table salt but also of smaller quantities of compounds of sodium, potassium and magnesium, was produced by the evaporation of great volumes of brine. Some of its deposits are large, one in north Germany being about 1,000 yards thick; excavations at Salzburg, Austria are extensive enough to resemble a large cave and the pumping out of the brine formed in the underground salt beds of Cheshire has produced serious subsidences. The salt becomes almost plastic under great pressure: it oozes down into crevices in the rocks and then is pressed up to form salt domes several miles across and thousands of feet deep.

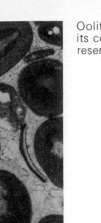

Oolitic limestone is so-called because its coarse granular structure was said to resemble the roe of a fish.

Limestone, although a sedimentary rock produced by the hardening of deposits on the sea floor, is very different in origin from sandstone and clay. It consists not of debris washed down from the rocks on the land but of the remains of sea-living creatures. These remains, however, were ultimately derived from the land, the skeletons and shells being largely formed of calcium carbonate from the remains of older limestone beds. The limestone consists almost completely of the mineral calcite (calcium carbonate). When pure this is perfectly white, but most of the limestone is tinted yellow-brown or reddish by iron and grey or black by other impurities. It varies in hardness, the more recently formed limestone blocks being soft enough to be cut with a knife, while the older beds have to be cut with a saw and those older still have to be quarried.

Sandstone and limestone alike may be naturally divided into rectangular blocks by joints (cracks) parallel and perpendicular to the bedding; they are then called freestones and such rocks are very convenient as building material. Weathering, and the percolation of rainwater into the limestone, tends to make these joints widen. The limestone is dissolved even by weak acid and so rainwater, which is a natural carbonic acid, has a considerable effect both above and below the surface.

Limestone contains many recognizable fossils and apart from these the bulk of this rock consists of grains of calcium carbonate, together with particles of sand from the silt, some of which are coated with calcium carbonate from the sea water. These grains vary in size: in oolite (roe stone) they are large enough to be visible to the naked eye and feel rough to the touch, so that oolitic limestone resembles the roe of a fish. The microscope shows that the grains consist of concentric layers of calcium carbonate centred on a grain of quartz, or on a tiny fragment of shell, or less frequently of seaweed. In pisolite, (pisolitic limestone is sometimes called pea grit), the grains are even larger.

Limestone may contain so many fossils that stretches of it seem almost to consist completely of them, especially as they may be harder than the rock itself so that weathering makes them stand out in bas-relief. Coral limestone may be so very fossiliferous that it may appear very much like a coral reef for the corals themselves consist of calcite. Shelly limestone contains fossils both of bivalve and univalve molluscs and of lampshells, animals superficially

A magnified section of oolitic limestone. These grains, large enough to make the rock feel rough to the touch, consist of concentric layers of limestone centred around a speck of quartz, or a tiny fragment of shell, or seaweed.

Shelly limestone in which a number of former seashells have been cemented into a rock.

This is corallian limestone, the remains of a former coral reef, now resistant enough to be used for building. The quarry is situated in Bermuda.

resembling the bivalves but completely different in bodily structure. Crinoidal limestone is largely built of the remains of the animals often inaccurately called sea lilies, and algal limestone contains fossilized seaweeds (algae).

These shells and other calcareous remains, like the animals from which they come, by no means consist only of calcium carbonate; they also contain silica, magnesium carbonate, calcium phosphate and other minerals. Their silica content precipitates to form chert (somewhat similar to the flint in chalk) and jaspar, which derives its bright colour from iron; both are found in the limestone. The chert, which may be fibrous in structure or formed of microscopic crystals, may occur in irregular beds roughly parallel to the layers of the limestone itself or in rounded masses. It may have seeped into the cracks and bedding planes of the rock while still in solution; and it may contain the remains of sponges and other animals.

Aragonite also consists of calcium carbonate and is a variant form of calcite: it is somewhat harder and heavier than calcite and it is not dissolved by rain water. Its crystals are differently shaped and this rock may be white, yellowish, grey or even green or violet. It is less stable than calcite into which it may gradually change.

Often associated with calcite or aragonite is magnesium carbonate, the two forming a combined carbonate, dolomite. Raised by earth movements this forms Dolomitic or Magnesian Limestone, named, like the Dolomites, an impressive mountain range in the Alps of the South Tyrol, after the French geologist Dolomieu. This rock is mostly honey coloured or brownish but can be tinged with brown or red, green or black and it too is rather harder and heavier than calcite. It is not very fossiliferous and may be associated with rock salt and gypsum.

Aragonite slowly changes into calcite, but calcite may change into dolomite, dissolving in sea water containing magnesium and then being redeposited. This might be regarded as a kind of metamorphism but it is more convenient simply to regard the dolomite as a hardened sediment.

Because calcite and its variants are so very porous the rocks they form are so deeply eroded by the rain that they stand out prominently above other beds. The rain forms few surface streams, however, and penetrates into its joint planes, carving the limestone into square or rectangular towers and pinnacles and terraces. In some regions, notably the Karst district of Yugoslavia, the rain falling on a level limestone surface traverses it with a series of perpendicular fissures, some of them quite deep, dividing it into a series of oblong blocks. The resulting rock pavement is a characteristic feature of limestone areas. Generally the calcite forms variegated hills which some people find austere and even repellent, although others find them delightful.

Chalk is the purest form of limestone and is usually white, almost dazzling in direct sunshine, but weathering grey on an exposed surface. There are, however, a few regions where the chalk has been tinted red by iron. Chalk greatly resembles the ooze on the sea floor, consisting of coccoliths (microscopic fossil plants) and their fragments in which larger fossils are embedded.

Chalk contains two minerals and the importance of one of these in human history has already been pointed out. Flint is a form of quartz; it is akin to chert, deposited on the sea floor by the silica contained in the remains of microscopic marine organisms. Its colour, however, is dark grey to black although it may weather to

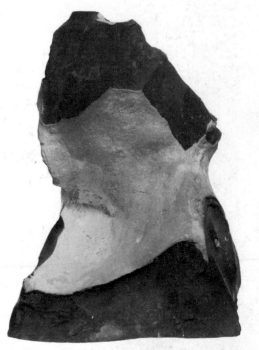

A flint, a concretion in chalk of silica (quartz), showing the contrast between its interior and its weathered surface. The white effect is produced by the scattering of the light by its minute particles.

Peat deposits, consisting of a spongy mixture of vegetable and earthy matter, are cut into turfs and stacked to dry. In some country districts these are used as a low grade fuel.

blue, and its surface, which consists of particles small enough to scatter light, is white.

Flint forms rounded masses mostly in lines parallel to the layers of the chalk and it breaks with a conchoidal (shell-like) fracture into two rounded surfaces, one concave and one convex. Some of the flints are hollow, forming geodes, and some of these are lined with amethyst, a purple variety of quartz. Others, called rotten by the quarrymen because they are unsuitable for building, contain a brown flint-meal, the detached spicules (spikes) of a sponge. Others contain fossils which are likewise converted into flint.

Nodules of marcasite may also be found in chalk. These are a form of iron pyrites and are spherical or cylindrical with rounded ends. They are brown on the surface and internally they are filled with a cluster of silvery needles, all radiating from the centre; these, however, soon rust on exposure to the air.

Chalk scenery is far less austere than that of limestone and consists of pleasant rolling hills. These are deeply trenched with river valleys and less deeply grooved by dry valleys, the beds of former streams eroded during periods of higher rainfall.

Coal is another sedimentary rock and consists of vegetable matter which in the course of time has been almost completely converted into carbon. During this process, however, it passed through several stages. Dead plant debris that falls into stagnant water is prevented from decaying by the lack of oxygen in the water and so its deposits can accumulate to form layers of peat. This consists of a spongy mixture of vegetable and earthy matter which after being cut into turfs and stacked to dry is used as a low-grade fuel in Ireland and elsewhere.

Left undisturbed and subjected to greater pressures by overlying material, the peat becomes progressively richer in carbon until it forms a variety of coal, lignite. This is also called brown coal, even though some of it is black in colour and although it is much more carbonized than peat, it still contains not only impressions but

actual leaves and other remains of the original vegetation from which it was formed. It has to be mined for and this is done extensively in Central Europe, in western Canada and in the Mississippi valley. A very hard variety of lignite which can take a high polish forms jet, which has been used from prehistoric times for decorative purposes.

When the vegetation has been completely compacted it produces several types of coal. Cannel coal is dark grey or black and although it has no lustre it too can be polished and used ornamentally. It contains much gas and burns with a smoky but very bright flame – hence the name candle coal – and can be distilled to produce oil. It includes no woody tissue but is seen under the microscope to have been formed from spores, pollen, seaweed and even some animal matter.

The usual household fuel varies greatly in texture and quality and although it contains no bitumen (pitch), it is called bituminous coal because it sometimes swells up like pitch while burning. It soils whatever it touches and some of its lumps bear the impressions of the bark, leaves or roots of the trees from which it was formed.

Anthracite is a high grade coal chiefly used for industrial purposes.

Very little indication of its vegetable origin is given by the best quality coal, anthracite, which contains very little gas and has been almost completely converted into carbon. It is very hard and shiny black in colour and although it will make marks it does not soil the fingers. Burning with a smokeless but very hot flame, it requires special types of stoves for domestic use and serves chiefly for industrial purposes.

Examination of the coal and of the beds of the Coal Measures, from which it is obtained, shows that it is derived from the fossilized remains of a succession of swampy forests which were repeatedly flooded by incursions of a shallow sea. Much of the coal comes from the latter part of the Palaeozoic Era, during a period known in Britain as Upper Carboniferous and in America as the Pennsylvanian.

Opposite Iron-stained sandstone showing the colouring shading into the unstained rocks above. Current bedding can also be clearly seen.

Opposite below Sand dunes consist of 'waves' of loose sand driven along by the wind. If cut into they may show a layered structure similar to the stratification in sandstone.

Left Limestone is quickly eroded by rainfall. The surface of this formation has been smoothed by the action of the weather.

Below The interbedding of white chalk with red chalk and Carstone (greensand) at Hunstanton on the coast of Norfolk.

Igneous and metamorphic rocks

A volcanic bomb, shot from the crater during the eruption of a volcano. Its rounded shape is caused by its rotation as it hurtled through the air in a molten state.

Even Werner, who insisted that the great majority of rocks had been formed on the ocean bed, could see that there were some exceptions, that certain rocks had been produced on the land, the most obvious being those due to volcanic action. He decided, however, that these were insignificant, that volcanic eruptions were not only rare but were temporary occurrences produced when a few local rocks had been melted by the heat produced when underground coal seams had caught fire. His opinions were refuted by the Scottish geologist James Hutton, whose *A Theory of the Earth*, published in 1802, stated that volcanoes serve as safety-valves for the intense heat within the Earth, allowing it to escape quietly without producing destructive earthquakes and other far-reaching earth movements. After much bitter argument his theory prevailed, with certain modifications.

The modern view of volcanoes is that they are caused by the uprush of masses of heated material under heavy pressure, not deep within the Earth but about twenty miles or so below the surface. As the pressure intensifies it forces some of the molten rock to escape; this thrusts itself up through the overlying rock beds until it bursts through the ground and produces a volcanic crater. The crater emits masses of the molten material: it includes the lava, a torrent of molten rock; smaller blobs forming spindle-shaped volcanic bombs; clouds of heated dust, often incorrectly called volcanic ash; floods of boiling water and clouds of steam and of such noxious gases as carbon dioxide and sulphur compounds.

Some of the volcanoes, like Stromboli in Sicily, are almost continually in operation. Others are dormant, not having erupted for periods which, geologically speaking, are recent. Others are apparently extinct, having shown no activity since much earlier in the geological record. A few, however, although dormant and apparently extinct, have suddenly erupted with extreme violence. Krakatoa, in the East Indies, broke out explosively after 200 years' inactivity in 1883. The most notorious of such eruptions was that of Vesuvius, whose true nature had never been suspected. In AD 79 it broke out with almost no warning and deluged Pompeii and Herculaneum with a flood of volcanic 'ash', and it has never since been totally quiescent.

The last manifestations of dying volcanic activity are shown by small openings in the ground which emit carbon dioxide and sulphurous fumes; by the geysers, notably those of Iceland, New Zealand and the Yellowstone National Park, Wyoming, USA, which spurt out jets of steam and boiling water; and by hot springs, whose waters are reputed to have medicinal properties. These outbursts of the Earth's internal heat leave marked impressions on their surroundings. Hot springs stain the rocks over which their waters flow and volcanic sulphur can accumulate in quantities large enough to be mined for industrial use. Cold water, exceptionally rich in calcite, coats the surroundings of its springs with a layer of calcareous tufa similar to the dripstone on a cave wall and to the fur that forms inside a kettle. Geysers form a layer of siliceous sinter, resembling the tufa but formed of silica.

Far greater than volcanic outbursts were the fissure eruptions, in which the ground opened not in a comparatively small crater but in a chasm several miles in length. This emitted the same material as a volcano, but its effects were more far reaching: the lava flow covered a greater area, and the showers of volcanic ash and noxious gases spread more widely. The most recent of these fissure eruptions occurred in Iceland in 1783.

In an ordinary eruption the lava and volcanic bombs pile up round the crater and together with lumps of rock ripped off from within the crater they form a conical hill, which grows larger as long as the lava continues to flow down its sides and to spread over the ground at its foot. The smaller fragments and the volcanic ash, really fine particles of lava hurled up by the eruption, are carried away by the wind. Any dust which falls on the sea drifts down to its floor, mingling with its sediment; that which drops on the land covers the surface with a coating of coarse grit and either resting on the sediment and grit or embedded in it are the volcanic bombs.

When the eruption dies down the lava in the crater cools and solidifies, plugging the vent with rock so hard that if the eruption recommences it may be unable to dislodge the plug and will break out in another crater. Earth movements may later bury a dormant or extinct volcano under layers of sedimentary rock. If further earth movements raise the former volcano to dry land it may be

The strange effects of erosion on basalt near Lake Myvatn, Iceland.

The encrustation by mineral deposits on rocks surrounding a boiling spring in Ethiopia.

Geysers are manifestations of the Earth's internal heat. These are at Rotura, New Zealand.

Left and below During a volcanic eruption, masses of molten rock consisting of material such as basalt are produced and smaller incandescent blobs of lava thrown up from the crater. These photographs show an eruption at Hekla, Iceland.

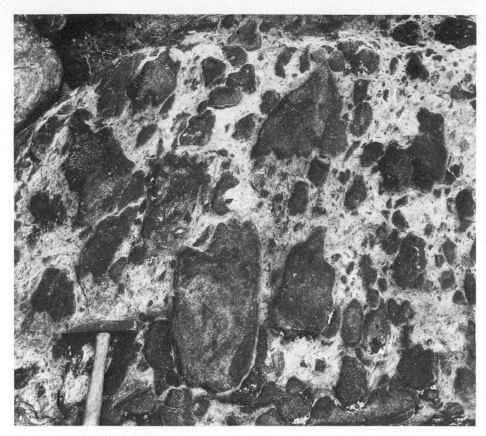

The ropy appearance of the upper surface of a lava flow (above) when the gases entrapped in it escaped quietly. This contrasts with the slaggy surface of a flow known from its appearance as breadcrust lava (below), produced as the molten basalt was chilled by the air above, or by the rocks over which it flowed.

more resistant to the weather than the overlying sedimentary rocks, and when these have been worn away it will remain as a hill of characteristic shape called a volcanic neck. When the central lava plug has been denuded of its covering it will protrude as a towering rock of unusual shape, also called a volcanic neck.

Necks of the first-named type form some striking features of Scottish scenery, Arthur's Hill and the Castle Rock of Edinburgh and the Dumbarton Castle Rock in the Firth of Clyde. Remarkable necks of the second type, with a fantastic resemblance to ruined castles and prehistoric monsters, occur near Lake Myvatn in the north of Iceland. Still more remarkable are some of the Puys in the Auvergne region of France, one 280 feet high bearing a church and another 435 feet high bearing a statue.

The dust and other fragments from the eruption which become immersed in the sea and later buried by sedimentary rocks, harden to form a volcanic agglomerate. The solidified lava, still called a lava flow, produces a very hard fine-grained layer of rock. Chilled by the rocks over which it flowed, its lower surface is slaggy; chilled by the air above, its upper surface is either slaggy, or if the gases entrapped in it escaped more quietly, this surface is ropy. The gases may have perforated the lava with numerous holes; if so it hardens into pumice. The holes may be elongated in the direction towards which the lava flowed and they may be filled with light-coloured minerals producing an amygdaloidal (almond-like) lava. Even if the agglomerate and the lava flow are buried by layers of sedimentary rock parallel to their own they are still recognizable. There are, however, several types of lava.

Although most lava resembles the well-known rock basalt, the influence of Werner long prevented the geologists from realizing the significance of this. He had taught that basalt had been part of the sludge hardened on the sea floor and some early geologists had found remarkable explanations for its columnar formations,

Right A fine-textured mass of obsidian, a natural glass of volcanic origin, from the Lebanon.

Opposite A formation of basalt showing its prismatic structure caused by its contraction as the rock cooled from a molten state. This is the Giant's Causeway in Northern Ireland.

Below Resistant sills composed of immense masses of basalt weather slowly and so form features of the landscape. Most of the Great Whin Sill in Northumberland, England, is hidden by overlying rocks but it forms a ridge along which Hadrian's Wall was built.

Obsidian (right) is a non-crystalline volcanic rock formed when the lava from a volcano cooled rapidly. In prehistoric times its hard fragments were worked into sharp edges and used in the manufacture of weapons for hunting. This compact form contrasts sharply with Pelé's Hair (below), a fibrous form of obsidian, produced by the lava spray of Mount Pelé.

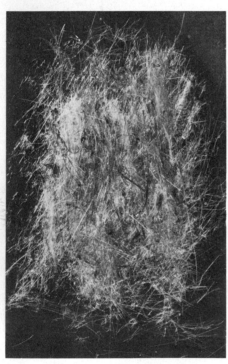

displayed, for example, in the Giant's Causeway in Northern Ireland and on the Island of Staffa in Scotland. They suggested that these hexagonal blocks must be huge crystals, no doubt originally topped with pyramids like those of quartz and calcite, or that they might possibly be petrified stems of a gigantic bamboo.

Tracing from their respective craters the many lava flows in the Auvergne region, the eighteenth-century French geologist Nicolas Desmarest ascertained, however, that the further they had travelled the more identical they were with basalt, and that some of them actually formed prismatic columns similar to those of the Giant's Causeway. It had at last to be agreed that the most common type of lava is identical with basalt.

Igneous rocks grade even more imperceptibly into one another than do the sedimentary rocks. They consist of a mixture of mineral salts, each formed by the combination of an acid with a base, the base being the heavier of the two. As the proportions of base and acid in the minerals that form the rock vary, so the rock changes not only in its weight but also in its character until it becomes an entirely different material.

Most of the lava flows consist of a hardened basalt. This is the lightest form of lava and when molten it was more fluid and spread more widely than the others. Flows of the Deccan Plateau basalts, India, cover 200,000 square miles and are 4,000 to 6,000 feet thick; those in the Columbia region of Idaho and Oregon, USA, are not so thick but they cover a greater area of 250,000 square miles; and those in the Paraná Basin in South America are estimated to contain about 50,000 cubic miles of rock.

Basalt consists of a medley of the minerals feldspar, olivine and augite with perhaps a little iron. If the olivine in a lava flow is replaced by hornblende and mica, the rock becomes andesite, whose colour varies from light to dark according to the proportions of the different minerals. If it contains a larger proportion of feldspar, some in lath-shaped crystals, its colour is still lighter and it is called trachyte. The next stage in the transition from a basic to an acid lava is rhyolite. This generally resembles granite in composition but its crystals are microscopic: it is formed of quartz, mica and feldspar with some hornblende and other minerals.

Another volcanic rock, obsidian, is a non-crystalline form of rhyolite formed when the lava had cooled very quickly. It resembles a black, brown or greenish bottle-glass; like flint it breaks into fragments with gently curved surfaces and sharp edges and like flint it was used by primitive man as a source of implements and weapons. A fibrous form of obsidian, produced by the lava spray of a volcano in the Hawaiian Islands, is known as Pelé's Hair.

Much of the molten material rising through the rocks never reached the surface. Forcing its way through narrow channels, it was barred by obstructions so that it cooled and hardened underground. The rocks thus formed are called intrusive, in contrast with the extrusive volcanic rocks although both are similar in composition. Some of these rocks fill the supply channels of former volcanoes, having risen up these until they were halted by a plug of solidified lava. As one would expect, the best explored of these pipes are in the diamond mines of South Africa. They are vertical or slightly oblique and they taper very gently downwards and are of unknown depth, none of them having been fully investigated. The greatest depth reached, in a pipe 600 feet across, is 3,600 feet.

A dyke, a vertical mass of basaltic rock, cutting through sandstone. The difference in character of the two rocks is very clear.

Sheets of molten rock also rose almost vertically and now form dykes of basalt cutting right through the sedimentary rock beds. They naturally weather at different rates from these and where they reach the surface they form either channels in the ground if the basalt were softer than the sedimentary rocks, or natural walls if it were harder. Such channels or walls may be up to half a mile wide and many miles in length. A number of dykes may occur together, either parallel or radiating from a centre. There are groups of parallel dykes in western Scotland and of radial dykes in the Cheviot Hills on the Scottish border; systems of parallel dykes in the United States occur at Spanish Peak, Colorado and the Crazy Mountains, Montana.

Some of these uprushes, after being almost vertical, were checked by a very resistant layer of the sedimentary rocks. They then swerved abruptly and continued below this bed and above the bed immediately below, forming a sill parallel to the other rock layers. Some of these sills again turned abruptly when the molten rock found a weak place in the rock layers above it, and rose steeply until it was once more checked by another resistant layer, returning to its earlier course parallel to the adjacent rock beds. Like the dykes, many of the sills were harder than the sedimentary rocks and so weathered more slowly to form marked features of the landscape.

In Yorkshire, England, the Great Whin Sill and the Cleveland Dyke build ridge across the country for many miles. The Great Whin Sill – basalt was once known as whinstone – is over 1,500 square miles in area, although most of it is hidden by the overlying rocks.

A sill has a general resemblance to a buried lava flow. Both form beds parallel to the layers above and below and both consist of basalt or some other hard fine-grained rock. They have, however, several important differences. The lower surface of the lava flow, unlike that of the sill, looks slaggy and its upper surface looks either slaggy or ropy. The flow bakes the rocks immediately beneath it and sends veinlets of lava into their crevices; the sill bakes and sends veinlets of basalt into the beds immediately above and below. The sill may change its horizon by passing through some of the layers above and resuming its direction at a higher level, but no lava flow does this.

Molten material from within the Earth also forces its way upwards in much greater volumes than that in dykes and sills. When checked by the immense weight of sedimentary rocks above, it neither cut a path through nor between them; instead it lifted these beds into an arch and formed a dome-shaped mass of molten igneous rock. Many domes resemble a sort of cistern in a large sill or at the top of a large channel rising from below, but in others, which seem to widen as their depths are investigated, the igneous rock extends indefinitely downwards.

Being far greater in volume than the material of dykes and sills and protected by the thickness of the overlying rocks from the chill of the air, the molten material in these bosses cooled much more slowly and so gave time for large crystals to form. Most of the igneous rock thus produced consists of granite, which corresponds in composition to rhyolite in spite of the difference in the sizes of their crystals. As already stated, granite consists principally of quartz, mica and feldspar, with smaller quantities of such minerals as fluorspar, tourmaline, garnet, topaz and iron. Although it forms innumerable crystals, the quartz seems also to fill the spaces

Porphyritic granite, so-called from the exceptional size of some of the quartz crystals. The smaller crystals consist of quartz, feldspar and mica.

between all the other crystals as though it were still cooling and solidifying after these had been formed.

The molten material in the bosses did far more than bake the adjoining rocks and fill their crevices; for some distance it completely altered their nature. Like the immense igneous formations in other lands, the granite boss which underlies Dartmoor is surrounded by a metamorphic aureole (halo), a mile or more wide, which largely consists of hornblende. In some of the bosses, on the other hand, igneous and sedimentary rocks have intermingled along the contact zone between them; here the granite contains syenite and other minerals such as garnet and epidote.

As the overlying sedimentary rocks are weathered away the granite boss is revealed and projects above the soil in formations like the granite tors. Although this rock does not show bedding, it exhibits joints produced by contraction on cooling, and some of the tors resemble cyclopean masonry; hence the term mural jointing (from *murus*, the Latin for a wall).

Once exposed to the air by the destruction of the overlying rocks, even the hard massive granite is attacked by the weather which smoothes its angles and widens its joints. It is as a result of this weathering process that the feldspar is decomposed by carbonic acid in the rain to form the clay kaolin. Large deposits of this occur in Cornwall where enormous greyish-white pyramids of spoil mark the presence of the china clay workings. Once the feldspar is destroyed, the other minerals are loosened and are soon washed away, exposing a new surface of the granite to the weather.

There are a number of different kinds of granite. The chief varieties are white and pink, these colours being that of the feldspar, but the glint of mica and the grey colour of quartz are also visible. The intermingling of the crystals gives some granites a strange suggestion of patterning. Some, the aplites, have a vague resemblance to sugar and orbicular granite displays banded circles formed by coloured minerals against a background of feldspar and dark mica. In graphic granite small crystals of quartz and feldspar, which must have been formed simultaneously, resemble some outlandish hieroglyphics. Quartz porphyry exhibits large crystals surrounded by smaller ones and other rocks may also be porphyritic.

In contrast with basalt, which is one of the most basic of rocks, granite is one of the most acid, and is consequently somewhat lighter. As its quartz content is increasingly replaced by other minerals, granite becomes less of an acid and more of a basic rock and increases in weight. In succession it blends into syenite, a dark reddish rock consisting of feldspar and mica with some hornblende or augite, roughly corresponding to trachyte; into diorite, resembling a small-grained andesite, grey or mottled green and white (greenstone), formed of feldspar, mica, and hornblende with perhaps some quartz; and finally into the basic rock gabbro, the equivalent of basalt, consisting of much feldspar with some augite and probably some olivine.

This difference in weight between granite and basalt throws light on the shape of the landmasses and on the Earth's geological history. The general similarity in outline of the coasts of western Europe and Africa with the coast of eastern America is obvious and indeed striking. They look as though they might almost fit into one another, as though they had once been continuous, and so, it is now concluded, they were.

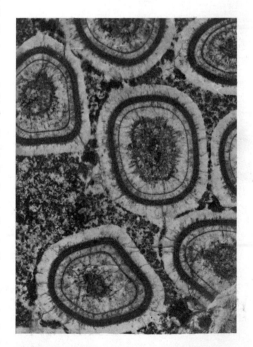

The concentric circles in orbicular granite are formed by coloured minerals, the remainder of the rock consisting of feldspar and dark mica.

Investigation has shown that the Earth consists of a central core of nickel-iron, under unimaginable conditions of temperature and pressure, which is surrounded by a mantle of silicate rocks outside which is the Earth's crust. This is formed by a layer of basaltic rocks, so hot that it is sufficiently plastic to flow sluggishly, and upon this plastic material lies the ocean and a discontinuous layer of granite which forms the land areas and supports the other rocks.

Powerful earth movements, probably arising from the expansion of the basalt within the crust when it was heated by its own radio-activity, split America off from the rest of a huge landmass to its east and forced it to move slowly westward. Similar changes split another great landmass centering on Antarctica into several segments and of these four drifted northwards. One, moving more slowly than the others, is now Australia; two united with the Eurasian landmass and became India and Africa; and the fourth merged with the first detached part of the great landmass to form the Americas. These movements also effected changes in the structure of these landmasses. As the Americas moved westward the rocks on their western end rose in a mighty ridge, now the Rocky Mountains and the Andes. Still greater were the mountains formed by the impact as India collided very slowly but with immense force with Asia: its highest part forms the Himalayas.

Such earth movements and the heat they generated, together with that of the molten material rising from below, naturally transformed the structure of the beds immediately involved producing the metamorphic rocks. Gneiss (pronounced nice), a characteristic metamorphic rock, is a granite whose minerals have been roughly sorted into separate layers giving the rock a banded appearance, alternately light and dark. Its bandings do not, however, form parallel layers like those of a sedimentary rock; they are in irregular undulating curves. Other materials from the rocks around have been blended into the gneiss and garnets and other minerals have also been produced. A batholith (an immense boss) in Idaho, about 16,000 square miles in area, consists not so much of granite as of gneiss, formed by the mixing of molten granite with the rocks from outside.

In schist the minerals have been even further separated into

Gneiss is a metamorphic rock produced by the action of intense heat and great pressure upon granite. This has produced the contortions in the minerals of which the rock is formed.

White marble in a quarry at Carrara, Italy. The limestone has been melted by great temperatures within the Earth and has recrystallized on cooling.

discontinuous layers which split and flake off readily (they have been compared to the flakes in puff pastry). Here again new minerals have been formed, notably garnet, kyanite and staurolite, and the schist itself includes materials from the sedimentary beds; hornblende schists, for example, are produced by the basic lavas. Clues to the composition of some schists are given by their appearance: a green colour indicates the presence of calcium and the familiar sheen of mica classes the rock as mica schist.

The ornamental rock serpentine, which is also a mineral, was formed by the metamorphism of rocks rich in magnesium, such as those containing olivine and amphibole. Soft enough to be readily worked into ornaments, it gives the Lizard, Cornwall, an important local industry and it also occurs in Scotland and in the eastern part of North America.

Some metamorphic rocks have been produced solely by heat. Marble is a limestone in which the calcite has melted, cooled and recrystallized (this process has been demonstrated in the laboratory). The limestone in the famous white marble of Carrara, Italy, was pure but the impurities in most limestones tint the marble attractively. Not all commercial marbles are genuine, however, some merely being limestones which will take a high polish; the so-called Purbeck Marble is made picturesque by the countless fossils in the limestone.

Hornstone, not to be confused with hornblende, is also a product of heat metamorphism of calcareous and sandy rocks, mostly very finely grained. This rock occurs in the metamorphic aureoles around granite bosses and as it has not been much affected by pressure it may show traces of the structure of the original rock.

A slate, on the other hand, is a shale which has been metamorphosed not by heat but by the pressure arising from earth movements; this has made the shale cleave (split) in a direction oblique to the original bedding. The layers into which the rock splits readily make it suitable for slating and other industrial purposes, and on some slates indications of the original bedding are still visible. Unlike almost all the other metamorphic rocks, slates may contain some fossils but the pressure has deformed most of these into strange, perhaps almost unrecognizable, shapes.

Rocks in outer space

Shooting stars, or meteors, which leave gleaming trails crossing the sky, appear either singly or in predictable swarms radiating from a common centre. Although it has long been established that objects resembling stones fall from the heavens and in 1492 a shooting star was credibly said to have done so at Ensisheim, Alsace, the possibility of such a thing was long denied. 'Stones do not fall from the sky', laughed Voltaire, 'because there are no stones in the sky.'

In 1803 the French scientist J. B. Biot verified, however, that a shower of such stones had actually occurred in the Normandy village of L'Aigle, and it is now quite clear that there must be stones in the sky because stones do fall from the sky, and that these are associated with shooting stars. Some have actually been seen falling and they may be accompanied by loud nerve-wracking crashes and other noises.

Although the shooting stars are known as meteors and meteor showers, from the Greek word meaning 'appearances in the upper air', the bodies that produce these appearances are called meteoroids, while those that fall to earth are named meteorites. The size of meteoroids varies greatly, from the microscopic upwards, but only the larger survive the intense heat generated by their rush through the atmosphere, which produces the incandescence that makes them visible; the smaller ones are completely destroyed by the heat and even those that survive have their surface burned away. There are three types of meteorites: the majority, the

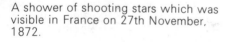

A shower of shooting stars which was visible in France on 27th November, 1872.

aerolites, consist of stone and of the others the siderites are iron, and the siderolites mixed iron and stone.

The largest fall on record is that of the Hoba siderite (all meteorites are named after the place where they fell – Hoba is in south-west Africa); and although much corroded it still weighs about sixty tons. The largest aerolite fell in 1948 in Norton County, Kansas, and weighed a ton. The greatest fall in the British Isles was that at Barwell, Leicestershire, in 1965, the largest aerolite to be picked up intact weighing over 100 pounds, although a shower in 1813, near Limerick, Eire, totalled over 106 pounds. The largest siderite, the Rowton, Shropshire, weighed only seven pounds and fell in 1876.

Many larger meteorites had fallen earlier and the very largest have never been recovered and are known only from the immense craters which their impact produced. Most descended only at gravitational speed, that of an ordinary fall from a great height, but some, although slowed by atmospheric resistance, retained most of the cosmic velocity with which they hurtled through space and this may be enough not only to produce a large crater but to vaporize the meteor itself.

The largest meteor crater is that in Arizona which is about 4,200 feet across and 570 feet deep. The meteorite whose fall produced it long ago is estimated to have weighed over a million tons, but the fall shattered and vaporized most of it: the Cañon Diabolo siderites formed by its fragments were scattered up to six miles.

Meteorites which fell in Saudi Arabia (above) and in the Punjab, India (below). In both instances the smooth surface was caused by the partial melting and recooling of the exterior as the meteorite fell at great speed through the atmosphere.

Meteor Crater, Arizona, USA, is about three-quarters of a mile across and 570 feet deep. The immense size of the meteorite and its great speed can be imagined from the fact that its fragments were scattered around within a radius of 6 miles from the crater.

Much larger must have been the Great Siberian meteorite which was seen and heard falling in 1908. Although not even a trace of its fragments has been discovered it produced many small craters and overthrew countless trees over a wide area. It has been surmised that if this really were a meteorite it must have been completely vaporized, whereas if it had been a comet it would have consisted almost entirely of gas and contained hardly any solid matter.

The heat generated as a meteorite speeds through the air melts its forward surface, which is scattered into droplets and partially vaporized and it is either given a smooth coating pitted with depressions rather like thumbmarks, or broken into angular fragments. This coats the siderites with a thin crust of magnetite (iron oxide), and the aerolites with a thicker layer of black glassy material including minerals such as olivine.

Each type of meteorite has several varieties. The siderites vary in their proportion of iron to nickel and in their crystalline structure. The siderolites are classed according to the type of silicate minerals mixed with their nickel-iron. Some of the aerolites contain spherical particles known as chondrules, formed of tiny mineral fragments, and the microscope reveals their structure as radiating from a centre. Most of the minerals which form these bodies are known to occur on earth; some of the chrondules in the aerolites even contain material including carbon. Among those which have not so far been detected elsewhere are schreibersite, a phosphide of nickel and iron, and troilite and perryite, sulphides respectively of iron and nickel.

Calculation shows that meteoroids travel round the sun in flattened elliptical orbits, some of which extend as far as the Zone of Asteroids, in which thousands of planetoids (minor planets) circle the sun between Mars and Jupiter. It has been suggested that all these bodies are the shattered remains of a large planet which formerly travelled in such an orbit, and that while some of its fragments still move in this zone, others hurled further afield have been captured by the gravitational pull of Jupiter or Saturn and now form some of their satellites, and that others became the meteoroids. This suggestion is supported by the age of the meteoroids (as indicated by a study of their radioactive decay products), which is roughly similar to that of the Earth, and also by their composition, which again resembles that of the Earth. The carbonaceous matter in some of the aerolites might indeed suggest that this former planet was possibly inhabited by living creatures.

Rounded fragments of glass of uncertain origin have been found in the East Indies, in the southern part of Australia and elsewhere. They were once thought to be obsidian, which they somewhat resemble, until it was realized that although this rock is a volcanic product the glass objects occur far from any volcano and that they are also somewhat different in shape. The radioactive decay products of these tektites shows that they were more recently formed than the meteorites, roughly at the age of certain of the Earth's rocks. Opinion is divided about the tektites and it is not known if they originate from the Moon, from the comets or from one of the planets. It seems more probable that they are terrestrial rocks that were fused and hurled into space by an explosion caused by the impact of a comet or an immense meteorite, and that they afterwards returned to the Earth. On the other hand, it has been computed that their distribution suggests trajectories emanating from

the crater Tycho near the centre of the southern part of the Moon's face. This theory has recently been abandoned, however.

There are other forms of natural glass, some resembling the tektites and others being composed of silica glass. Many of the latter were found in the Libyan Desert, and appear to be formed by fused desert sand, although what could have caused this fusion is unknown.

Tektites are pieces of natural glass rich in silica. They resemble obsidian but they occur many miles from any volcano and they differ in shape and in the patterns produced in their structure by erosion. Their exact nature and origin are in fact still under dispute.

A specimen of lunar rock about 2 inches across. This is medium to fine-grained, vesicular crystalline rock of igneous origin.

Since the time of Galileo it has been known that the Moon is a world with certain resemblances to the Earth, and within recent years it has been explored, first by means of instruments launched by the Russians and then at first hand by several teams of American astronauts. Specimens of Moon rocks have been brought back to Earth for detailed analysis.

These investigations verify that great areas, miscalled seas, are really deserts. As the Moon is devoid of any atmosphere its rocks cannot be weathered but the surface is swept by solar winds composed of streams of electrified particles hurled outwards from the sun, and bombarded by the mysterious cosmic rays whose origin and nature are not yet understood. These may have caused the immense lava flows which extend for many miles across the Moon's surface. The lack of atmosphere and therefore presumably of life on the Moon means that there can be no true soil on its surface. Its place is taken by the arid regolith, a layer of fragments from the rocks below, in some regions several yards deep. These are mostly basaltic in type and the fragments seem to be freshly crushed although there are also breccias present; there is also a quantity of granitic rock.

The moon has long been known to be covered with innumerable craters. Some were produced by the impact of meteoroids, which because of the lack of atmosphere, crashed down at cosmic velocities even greater than those which fall on Earth. Their impact generated an intense heat sufficient perhaps to vaporize the meteoroids and part of the Moon's surface. Other craters may have

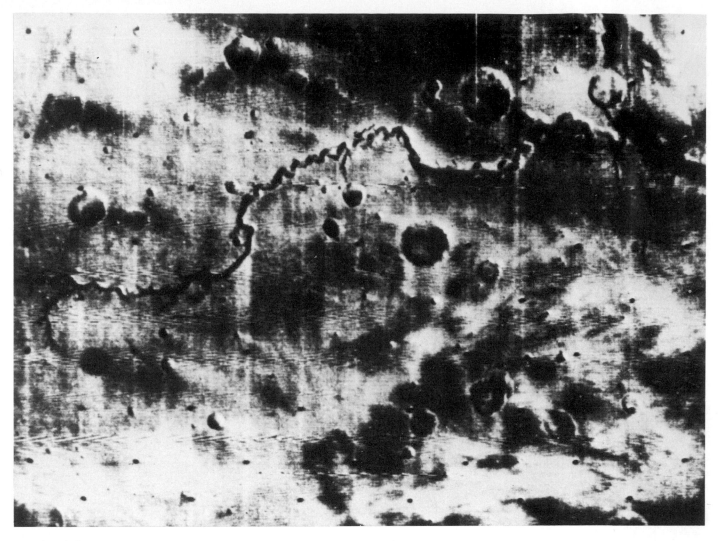

resulted from volcanic eruptions or from bubbles of gas generated below the surface. What have been called cosmic beads, hardened drops of glass or metal, have also been discovered on the Moon and space capsules fallen two years previously were found by astronauts to be already coated with dust.

It now seems probable that the Moon originated from the condensation of a cloud of particles which once encircled the Earth, somewhat similar to the rings around Saturn.

Among the minerals present on the Moon are feldspar, olivine, ilmenite, pyroxene and grains of iron. There is a large proportion of minerals present with high melting points, chromium, titanium, ytterbium and zirconium, but few with low melting points such as lead, bismuth, sodium or potassium. There are many inert gases, produced by radioactive decay caused by the solar winds, for example, argon, helium, neon, krypton and xenon.

The planet Mars has recently been photographed and views of its surface have been transmitted back to Earth from unmanned space capsules. Its surface in some ways resembles that of the Moon, being pitted with craters produced by the impact of meteorites, and it is swept by fierce dust storms which may be responsible for changes in its colour visible from the Earth. It also shows evidence of water erosion, however, including deep canyons and water courses. There are also the remains of huge volcanoes and volcanic action may not have ceased completely: it is suggested that what seem to be clouds of water vapour may have emerged through volcanic vents.

This photograph of a surface feature on Mars was taken in space from an unmanned spacecraft and transmitted to Earth. The feature resembles a giant version of a watercut gulley, such as those found in the south west of the United States, although it was supposed that the planet was completely dry.

Prospectors panning for gold, the
method probably used from the dawn of
history. This photograph was taken in
California, USA, where a gold rush
occurred in 1849.

Mining and mineral characteristics

It has been explained that almost all the rocks are varied in their composition, one blending imperceptibly into another. All, however, are formed of minerals, and the composition of the great majority of these and their chemical and physical properties is definite. Although all rocks consist of minerals, the greatest variety of these occur in those rocks which are of igneous origin and among these are found almost all the ores and other minerals of greatest interest and industrial use.

The molten material which forced its way through the sedimentary beds was so intensely hot that some of it was vaporized; the boiling water consisted of solutions of certain minerals some of which were so acid that they dissolved others. When the vapour was chilled either by the air or by contact with the cool sedimentary rocks through which it passed, most of it first condensed into a hot liquid and then became solid, although some of it solidified at once without passing through the liquid state and was deposited as a sublimate on the rocks around. With very few exceptions, the various minerals formed crystals, large when they cooled slowly, microscopic when they solidified rapidly; they did not cool simultaneously but some in advance of others, their crystals forming a lining on the walls of the channels they had traversed.

Before it solidified, some of the vapour or molten matter penetrated not only into the channels and cracks in the sedimentary rocks but also between their minutest grains. This metamorphosed these beds and produced other minerals so that an igneous mass may end not abruptly but in a zone of mixed igneous, metamorphic and sedimentary rocks.

When the surface of the rocks is eroded by weather the minerals within them may be resistant enough to survive. Set free by the destruction of the beds around them, they may be washed out by the rain and swept down to the sea by rivers. Smoothed by friction but still intact, they may be deposited on the way in the shallows of the rivers or on the beaches at its mouth.

In the distant past, gleaming or brightly coloured fragments probably caught the eye of primitive wanderers and were collected either for personal adornment, for magical reasons or for both. It may have been thus that the precious metals and the gems first acquired their value; the glint of gold suggesting the radiance of the sun, the glitter of silver that of the moon and the glimmer of the gems that of the stars. Whatever the reason, ornaments made of precious metal and gemstones figured in the barter carried on in primitive times and are found in the remains of Stone Age settlements. Copper, some of which occurs native (not in compounds

This illustration from Agricola's *De Re Metallica* shows the techniques employed in the sixteenth century by the miners of Germany: the detection of lodes with a divining rod, the working of the face, and the transporting of the ore.

but as an element), may have been mistaken for a sort of gold, and the hardness of native iron would at once be found useful.

The casual collecting of metals and gemstones may have gradually led to a systematic attempt to find them. This may have included 'placer mining', the river sediments being sifted in the hope that they might contain gold dust or silver or tin, or some of the gems, and ingenious methods were devised of extracting any treasure which they held. One of these methods inspired a well-known Greek legend: it is thought that Jason's Quest for the Golden Fleece was based on an historical search for a literal fleece, a sheepskin used to trap gold dust which the rivers washed down from Colchis, a mountainous region believed to exist somewhere south-east of the Black Sea. This method is quite practical: as the heavy particles of gold get entangled in the wool of a modern blanket or the hairs of a fleece, the light silt is washed away.

Another method, even more primitive, is to sift the silt with the fingers or in any suitable implement. Modern prospectors use a shallow pan, scooping up the silt and then giving the pan a swirling motion and tilting it slightly. While the silt is washed over the edge the pebbles stay in the pan, and if there are any nuggets in this pay-dirt they can be picked out; any gold dust present can also be extracted. This simple process can readily be mechanized. Where there is much gold, as there was in the Klondike territory in northern Canada, or much tin, as there is in the rivers of Malaysia, the silt can be led into a sloping trough or into a 'jigger' shaken by machinery. Alternatively it can be scooped up bodily by dredgers and dumped into sluices. The earth can be washed away by a powerful jet of water, or the river can be diverted into an artificial channel. Rich pay-dirt may indicate the existence of a gold reef (vein) or a deposit of tin further upstream.

When a mineral is discovered not in the placers but in the rocks themselves then, as the term mineral implies, it has to be mined for. The simplest method which could have been used with crude implements in prehistoric times was opencast mining: first the topsoil or other overburden had to be removed and then the mineral could be hewn out. This again lends itself to mechanization and opencast mines are now cut several hundred feet deep.

When a bed of mineral deposit slopes obliquely downwards opencast mining has to give way to deep mining, and here again techniques have become increasingly complicated. Still, however, they are based upon the methods of the pre-mechanical past, as is made clear in a book published in 1556. The author of *De Re Metallica* (Concerning Things Metallic) was a German mining engineer, Georg Bauer. He wrote, as was then the custom, under the Latinized version of his name, Agricola (peasant); he also produced other books on rocks and the 'fossils', a term which formerly covered anything dug out of the ground, but this is the only one of his works translated into English. An enthusiast for his vocation, the winning of the Earth's metallic treasures for the service of man, he has aptly been called the Father of Mineralogy.

Agricola describes and illustrates methods of tracing the veins of deposits and of excavating the mine workings, ventilating them and preventing their sides or roofs from collapsing. He also discusses the use of the divining rod although he himself had little faith in it. It has been used with success in modern times but this may depend not on the rod itself but on some form of the user's extra-sensory perception.

As the more accessible deposits are exhausted and the workings have to be driven deeper and deeper, with growing risks of accident and increasing difficulties in keeping the workings ventilated and free from water, mining techniques become correspondingly complicated. Minerals are now reached by means of a vertical shaft sunk into the ground and carefully buttressed lest its sides should cave in; or less frequently by an adit, a horizontal or gently sloping tunnel driven in from the side of a hill. Horizontal galleries are then excavated to reach the deposits of ore, and here, as well as in the adit, the roof as well as the sides have to be strengthened to prevent any subsidence of the rocks. The ore has then to be hewn away, conveyed along the galleries to the shaft and raised to the surface.

Even before Agricola's time human labour was supplemented by that of animals and by ingenious machinery driven by treadmills or by wind and water power. These methods proved increasingly inadequate as the mines had to be sunk deeper and deeper, with ever increasing difficulty in raising men and materials to the surface and in pumping out the water which constantly accumulates underground. In Britain something more effective was needed both in the coal mines and the Cornish tin mines, and attempts were made to harness steam power but it was only when early steam engines were perfected by James Watt that the winning of coal and the ores could be mechanized.

The revolution which the steam engine produced in human affairs has already been mentioned and its effects on mining tech-

One of the mid-nineteenth century Cornish tin mines showing the engine houses and a beam engine pumping out flood water from the workings.

The early apparatus of the early copper and tin mines was superseded by the more efficient methods made possible by the use of steam. This early print depicts a copper mine.

niques were no less far reaching. The mines are now lit, supplied with fresh air and freed from flood water, the coal or ore is excavated and raised to the surface, and the miners are conveyed to and from their work, by a host of complicated mechanical and electrical devices. However, human labour and peril have not and never will be banished completely from the industry although they have been greatly reduced.

Each of the minerals demands its own extraction technique. Gold is no longer won exclusively by the old placer method. The rocks in which the native metal occurs, as well as its ores, are crushed and mixed with water to form a paste. This is then amalgamated with mercury, or if the metal is very finely divided it is combined with potassium cyanide, and with either process further treatment is needed to separate the gold.

Primitive man found copper ores almost smelted themselves for the heat of a fierce woodfire soon exceeds the metal's melting point. But was this discovered entirely by accident as is often supposed? Men of ingenious mind lived in the Stone Age and they may have been impressed with the changes which cooking produced in food and with the baking of clay into earthenware, and set out to discover what other transformations the heat of their fires might produce. Even if the smelting of copper as well as that of tin were hit upon by accident, the discovery that when these two were combined they produced a metal which was much more useful than either was surely the result of intelligent experiment; the first alloy, bronze, is much harder than copper and does not lose its edge so quickly.

Modern industry demands smelting methods better suited to mass production and although it is fairly easy to smelt the carbonates and oxides of copper in a blast furnace, its sulphides demand much more complicated techniques. The different ores of copper and the other metals will be described later.

As in prehistoric times, iron is today more intractable than most of the other metals; to smelt its ores is difficult and to convert the iron into steel even more so. In the Middle Ages, pig iron, the metal in its first crude form, was still produced by smelting the ore

in a charcoal fire by the aid of an air blast from bellows worked by waterwheels. In addition, it needed further complicated treatment before it was fit for use. Although charcoal was replaced by coke and coke by coal, steel could be manufactured in bulk only after Bessemer, in the middle of the nineteenth century, invented the comparatively simple method of freeing molten pig iron from its impurities by blowing cold air through it in a special furnace. From being material for a craftsman, iron is now produced in great quantity and in a variety of types, including its many alloys with certain other metals.

Coal is not a true mineral in the geological sense but the mining of this and other 'mineral fuels' involves special difficulties, which can be mentioned only briefly here. The ordinary hazards of work underground are increased in coal mines by the gases which the coal exudes. Choke-damp consists of carbonic acid gas of lethal strength, as does the after-damp produced by an explosion of fire-damp, carburetted hydrogen, which is ready to ignite at a spark. Electric lighting and the safety lamp of course greatly reduced these risks but these have not been eliminated altogether.

Oil and natural gas are thought to be largely of organic origin, formed by the decay of immense accumulations of the remains of plants and animals. They seep into such permeable beds as sands, sandstones and muds surrounded by impermeable rocks much after the style of underground water with the difference that where-as water makes its way downwards gas and oil make their way upwards. Being under immense pressure, they are ready to spurt out as a gusher which has to be plugged and piped until as the pressure subsides the oil may have to be pumped out. Flames arising from the earth have long been known, and drilling for oil began in China about 200 years BC. This is now practised on a large scale, surface indications showing where the fuels are most likely to be found. However, drilling is also carried out beneath the sea from oil rigs mounted on floating platforms, the most recent development being the tapping of natural gas beneath the North Sea.

Before any mineral can be worked it has to be identified, and the

Gold mining of the present day. This great dredger used in Alaska may be contrasted with the crude methods of panning employed in the days of Jack London and Robert W. Service.

simple methods used by the early prospectors were generally similar to those used today by amateur geologists and by rock-hounds in search of ornamental stones. Amplified by mining engineers, they form the basis of the techniques employed by mining companies of the present day. Experience showed the prospectors that the metals were far more numerous than they had supposed. Agricola recognized the existence of antimony and bismuth and about the end of the eighteenth century Werner gave a list of about a score. Today about three dozen are known.

The early prospectors, like the modern geologists, were first attracted by the appearance of a mineral and then used this as a clue to its nature. They considered not only the mineral's colour but also its lustre, the bright or feeble gleam of its surface, and its transparency or translucency. Appearances, however, can be misleading and the early prospectors must soon have learned through bitter experience that 'all that glitters is not gold': the brassy hue and metallic lustre of iron pyrites no doubt deceived them just as it could deceive the modern tenderfoot in recent gold rushes. Colour, moreover, can be masked by impurities or concealed by superficial tarnish, and some minerals may have several different hues.

The feel of a mineral also helps in its identification: its weight, its hardness or softness, and the smoothness or roughness of its surface; a few minerals have a slight but perceptible smell which increases when they are heated, and there is no mistaking the taste of rock salt, nor its characteristic of attracting water from the air and dissolving into a puddle of brine.

Modern geologists have greatly refined the methods of identifying a mineral by its feel. Its weight is now defined as its specific gravity, its relative weight as compared to the weight of an equal volume of water. In the field this still has to be estimated roughly, but at home or in the laboratory it can be ascertained with very simple apparatus.

For hardness values Mohs' scale is used: this enables the mineral's hardness to be compared with that of others. Minerals are classified on a scale from 1 to 10, soft to hard, and all these grades are represented on the scale by well-known minerals: 1 talc; 2 rock salt or gypsum; 3 calcite; 4 fluorspar; 5 apatite; 6 orthoclase feldspar; 7 quartz; 8 topaz; 9 corundum; 10 diamond. A set of hardness pencils, metal rods tipped with one or other of these minerals, is obtainable, but without these hardness can be judged more simply by the method described in the final chapter.

Other tests which can be used in the field include a mineral's streak, the colour of the mark which it leaves on a streak plate, a small piece of unglazed porcelain or roughened glass; this may or may not be identical with the colour of the mineral itself. The fracture or cleavage of a mineral, the method in which it breaks or splits, also helps in its identification and magnetic properties or the emission of radioactivity are other valuable guides.

In the eighteenth century Werner published a treatise on the identification of minerals based not on their chemical composition but on their physical properties. This did much to establish mineralogy as a science, but for a full discussion of this, the enquiring reader must be referred to the larger and more technical works on the subject.

Early man, always on the look-out for minerals like gold and precious stones, must have been attracted by the crystals formed

by such minerals as calcite, fluorspar and quartz. The Greeks regarded the transparent variety of quartz as ordinary ice which had somehow become so completely frozen that it refused to thaw; hence they called it *krustallos* (clear ice), and it is still known as rock crystal. Several of the pioneer geologists, including Werner, discussed crystals, but it was Werner's French contemporary, the Abbé René Haüy, whose genius, it was said, 'raised mineralogy to the rank of a science'. Haüy first noticed that when broken by the happy accident of dropping a good specimen on the floor, the six-sided pyramids of calcite smashed into several smaller crystals and that these then formed tiny rhombohedra, each with faces at the same angles as those of the crystals of another form of calcite, Iceland spar. Thereupon, it is said, he deliberately smashed all the crystals he could lay hands on and was delighted to find that these likewise broke into smaller ones.

In 1801 Haüy published his theory that crystals are built up of innumerable minute units which he called 'bricks' and that the different forms of the minerals depend on the arrangement of these units. His theory still stands although it has been greatly modified, for his idea of the arrangement of units has been superseded by that of atomic groups. One later mineralogist declared that he was able to deduce the chemical composition of about 10,000 substances simply by examining their crystals.

Just as a sphere may be regarded as built round its axis, so the crystals are thought of as based on three or four intersecting axes. There are six crystal systems comprising thirty-two types of symmetry with several solid forms in each; only one of these has an everyday name, the cube, and others include tapering pyramids and flat-sided prisms.

It was the transparency and clearness of this form of silica (quartz) which earned it the name rock crystal, bestowed on it in classical times by the ancient Greeks.

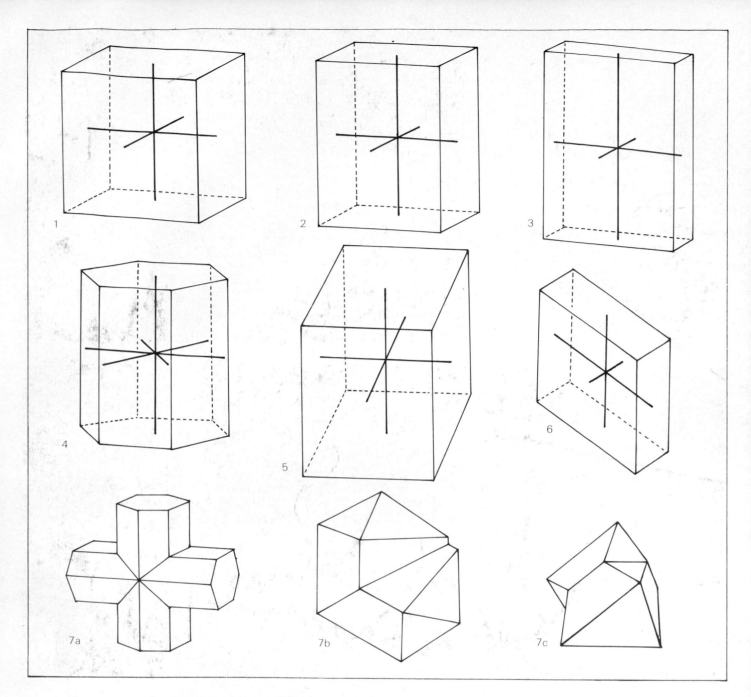

The crystals in the cubic system have three axes, all equal and at right-angles to one another. The axes in the tetragonal system are also at right-angles, but only two of them are equal whereas all three axes in the orthorhombic system are again at right-angles, but here no two are equal. Crystals in the hexagonal system have four axes of which three, separated by angles of 120°, are equal while the fourth is perpendicular to them. All three axes in the remaining two systems are unequal; in the monoclinic system two are at right-angles, the third being oblique and in the triclinic all the axes are oblique to one another.

One seldom finds the perfect crystals depicted in many text book illustrations. Many minerals also occur massive (in shapeless lumps); their exposed surfaces may display a crystal face or two, and if so these faces and the angles at which they meet will conform to the text book. So will those of the crystals which occur in clusters, several springing from a common base. Composite crystal forms also occur and here the tendency of crystals to split along definite planes related to their internal structure must be taken into

Drawings to illustrate the six basic crystal systems and twinned crystals:
1 cubic, 2 tetragonal, 3 orthorhombic, 4 hexagonal, 5 monoclinic, 6 triclinic, 7 crystal twins of a) staurolite (orthorhombic), b) zircon (tetragonal) and c) spinel (cubic).

account. In most crystals cleavage is parallel to the faces but fluor-spar, which crystallizes in cubes, cleaves across their corners, parallel to the faces of an octahedron.

Some crystals are twinned and seem to grow out of one another; in lamellar twinning they alternate in thin layers, so that the edge of the crystals seems to be finely ruled with parallel lines. Crystallization is no mere surface matter, however, for it extends through the whole mineral. It is best seen in the laboratory when a thin slice of a mineral, mounted on a glass slip, is observed under polarized light in a petrological microscope. The crystals, almost indistinguishable in ordinary light, then appear quite distinctly, and some are in bright colours, so that certain rocks display almost an entrancing beauty.

In the following chapters in which minerals are described individually, hardness (expressed as a value on Mohs' scale) and specific gravity will be shown in the following abbreviations: (H $2\frac{1}{2}$; SG 4). Streak, lustre, cleavage and crystal form will also be described.

Examples of crystals of four of the six crystal systems. Top left iodocrase (tetragonal), top right barytes (orthorhombic), bottom left beryl (hexagonal), bottom right axinite (triclinic).

66

Above A modern opencast copper mine in Zambia.

Left Panning for gold in northern Finland.

Opposite An old winding beam-engine used in the Cornish tin mines.

Metallic minerals

In 1817 Werner published a list of the minerals then known, 317 in all. He classified the metallic minerals separately from the others, treating them under their respective metals, of which he recognized twenty-two. Now that over 1,000 minerals are known, far too many to be mentioned individually, his method is still useful. In this book, the ores, the metallic minerals, are discussed separately from the others, but the gemstones separately from both; their order takes into account both their economic importance and their general or technical interest.

Only about six metals were known in the ancient world. For mystical reasons all nature was assumed to run in sevens and these metals were associated with what were then called the heavenly bodies. After all, it seemed reasonable to assume that gold had something to do with the sun and silver with the moon, so why should not the other metals be associated with planets? The traditional signs used on astronomical and astrological charts still serve to indicate the presence of the appropriate metals and their ores on geological maps. The somewhat similar signs later used for some of the other minerals have now all been superseded by formulae denoting their chemical composition.

Many other metals have since been discovered, some quite recently, but many of them would hardly be recognizable as metals in those days because of their very unmetallic appearance. Most of those included in this chapter look and feel like metals: they are the ores, the minerals from which the metals are obtained.

From very early days the most important metal in human life has been iron, and it is certainly the most important in nature. Steel weapons were so much more efficient than bronze that they were a terror in themselves and so this may have been the reason that iron is associated with Mars, the God of War. Steel builds our railroad tracks, our ships and bridges and other necessities, from the frames of our concrete buildings to our so-called tin cans, really made of tinned iron. Iron, associated with nickel, constitutes many of the meteorites and forms the core of our own earth.

On the Earth's surface iron occurs native (uncombined with other elements) in small quantities and in combination it forms a number of ores of which one of the most important is magnetite or magnetic iron ore. Its mysterious power of attracting or adhering to iron or steel objects aroused awed attention and inspired such legends as that of the Magnetic Mountain, which would sink any ship that ventured near it by ripping out all its iron nails and bolts; in sober earnest, a deposit of magnetite can still imperil a traveller by its action on his compass.

The characteristic shape and red colour of haematite have earned it the name of kidney iron ore.

Magnetite, which is an oxide of iron (Fe_3O_4), is itself iron-black, with a black streak and a metallic lustre. It belongs to the cubic system, forming eight-sided octahedra or twelve-sided crystals, and also occurs in grains and, of course, massive. It cleaves imperfectly but has a chonchoidal fracture and, as one would expect, it is hard and heavy (H $5\frac{1}{2}$ to $6\frac{1}{2}$; SG 5). It is found in Britain and America and many other countries.

Another important ore of iron is haematite (Fe_2O_3), which is also known as specular iron and as kidney ore from the brightness of the lustre it sometimes shows and from its rounded shape. It is steel-grey to iron-black in colour and its streak is cherry-red. It crystallizes in the hexagonal system forming six-sided solids like cubes which have been pressed somewhat askew; it is about as hard and heavy as magnetite (H $6\frac{1}{2}$; SG 5). Its earthy form, reddle, is used as the basis for red paint and red crayons. Haematite occurs in Britain in Cumberland and in the Forest of Dean on the Welsh border, and in greater abundance in several regions of the United States, notably near Lake Superior.

Limonite is another oxide of iron ($2Fe_2O_3 . 3H_2O$) but it is an

Limonite, or brown haematite, is a hydrated oxide of iron. This may occur in seams or in rounded masses.

Native copper: not an ore but consisting of the metal itself. This often occurs in tree-like forms or in confused threads.

hydrated oxide, the ore also containing water. Because of its colour and streak it is known as brown haematite. It has no crystalline structure but occurs in rounded masses or in tapering forms resembling stalactites, or it may be loose and earthy; it is about as hard as magnetite but is not quite so heavy (H 5 to $5\frac{1}{2}$; SG $3\frac{1}{2}$ to 4). As the loose porous substance which forms in and discolours the water of swamps it is called bog iron ore, and when it forms nodules it is called pea iron ore; it yields the brown or yellow ochres used as paints. Limonite produces important deposits in Spain and Cuba and in Sweden six inches of bog iron ore have accumulated in less than thirty years.

Iron pyrites is iron sulphide (FeS_2) and has acquired the nickname 'fool's gold' because its brassy colour and lustre have misled many an unwary prospector. Its streak is greenish or brownishblack and it crystallizes in the cubic system in cubes or in a characteristic form known as the pyritohedron. The faces of the cubes may be striated, the striations on one face being at right-angles to those on another; it is about as hard as haematite but is somewhat lighter (H 6 to $6\frac{1}{2}$; SG 5). It occurs in many regions including the United States and in the Cleveland Hills, England it has an oolitic (coarse-grained) structure.

Marcasite, white iron pyrites, is identical in composition with pyrites and has the same hardness and weight, but its colour is lighter and its streak is greyish. It crystallizes in the orthorhombic system, forming unusually shaped crystals including twins, some of them grouped together in cockscomb and spear pyrites. It also produces the brown nodules containing radiating silvery needles found in the English chalk.

Chalybite is iron carbonate ($FeCO_3$) and forms beds or nodules in the Coal Measures and other formations of Britain, the United States and elsewhere. It is coloured various shades of brown and has a white streak. It belongs to the hexagonal system but is often found massive and is of medium hardness and weight (H $3\frac{1}{2}$ to $4\frac{1}{2}$; SG $3\frac{1}{2}$ to 4). As clay ironstone it used to be worked in The Weald in the south-east of England and as oolitic ironstone, in the Cleveland iron ore, it has replaced and adopted the grained texture of oolitic limestone.

Copper, which melts at a comparatively low temperature, was probably one of the first metals to be discovered. Although it was soon superseded for tools and weapons first by bronze and then by iron, it was still used for domestic purposes: a polished sheet of copper could be used as a mirror, so it is easy to see why copper was assigned to Venus, the planet of the Goddess of Love. Copper is, of course, of great importance as a conductor in the electrical industry and in electrical machinery. It also enters into many alloys, not only bronze but gunmetal, bellmetal, brass and others of special technical importance, and it has other industrial uses.

Copper occurs native, for example, near Lake Superior in the United States, and also in a number of ores, mostly of a striking colour. Its principal ore is copper pyrites, chalcopyrite, a sulphide not of copper alone but of both copper and iron ($CuFeS_2$). This has a brassy appearance and is sometimes made more variable by an iridescent tarnish; it has a greenish-black streak. It belongs to the tetragonal system but is usually massive and its crystals resemble cubes or wedges and may be twinned; it is of medium softness and weight (H $3\frac{1}{2}$ to 4; SG 4). It occurs in many parts of the world, notably in the western part of North America, and in Cornwall.

Copper pyrites from Queensland,
Australia. Its coloured tarnish is quite
apparent.

Sphalerite, also called zinc blende and
black jack, the most common ore of zinc,
often occurs in association with galena,
lead ore.

Chalcopyrites (copper pyrites — an ore of iron and copper) on large quartz crystals.

Here, it was recently announced in the Press, indications of what may be an important new strike of copper have recently been discovered.

Another sulphide of copper and iron, bornite or variegated copper ore (Cu_5FeS_4), may be associated with copper pyrites, as in Mansfeld, Germany. It is copper coloured with a pale greyish-black streak and a metallic lustre. Bornite crystallizes in the cubic system in cubes or eight-sided octahedra, but it is usually massive and is heavy and of medium hardness (H 3; SG 5 to $5\frac{1}{2}$). When made iridescent by tarnish it is known as peacock ore and in Cornwall it is also called horse-flesh ore.

Two especially beautiful ores of copper are hydrated carbonates, the green malachite ($CuCO_3 . Cu(OH)_2$), and the blue chessylite or azurite ($2CuCO_3 . Cu(OH)_2$); their streaks are somewhat lighter in colour and their lustre varies. Both crystallize in the monoclinic system but are usually massive; malachite may have a rounded surface with concentric bands of colour and both are of medium hardness and weight (H $3\frac{1}{2}$ to 4; SG 4).

The red oxide of copper, cuprite (Cu_2O), has a brownish-red streak. It belongs to the cubic system, forming eight- or twelve-sided crystals and is heavy and hard (H $3\frac{1}{2}$ to 4; SG 5). Its varieties are the crystalline ruby copper, the earthy reddish-brown tile ore and the fibrous interlaced crystals known as chalcotrichite, from the Greek for copper hair.

Some copper ores are less spectacular. The grey coppers comprise several sulphides in which copper is associated with iron, antimony or arsenic. In another grey sulphide, bournonite ($CuPbSbS_3$), the copper is associated with lead and antimony and is unusual for the shape of some of its twinned crystals, which

have earned it the name of wheel ore. These sulphides have a grey to black colour and streak and are of medium hardness but rather heavy (H $2\frac{1}{2}$ to $4\frac{1}{2}$; SG 6).

Tin, which also has a very low melting point, seems to have been discovered soon after copper and its value in forming the much more efficient bronze alloy was soon realized by the early metallurgists. It was probably its brightness which caused it to be associated with the radiant planet Jupiter, the Father of the Gods, for it is difficult to imagine any other reason. It is now used not only in bronze but in several other alloys employed in metal bearings, type metal and pewter. Its use in making thin sheets of iron rustproof gives us tin plate utilized in domestic cans.

The only important ore of tin is tinstone which is also known as cassiterite because in classical days it was imported from the tin islands (Casseritides), as the Carthaginian traders called Britain. It is still mined in Cornwall, where fragments of the ore eroded by

Tinstone, tin oxide, forms tetragonal crystals and is also known as cassiterite. It is the only important source of tin.

Opposite Wulfenite, a combination of lead and molybdenum. These bright yellow tabular crystals on a matrix are from Mexico.

Opposite below The silver-white colour of native silver readily tarnishes and although very heavy it is quite soft.

Right Bournonite, a sulphide of copper, lead and antimony. The curious shape of some of its crystals earned it the name wheel ore.

A vein of lead ore lining a fissure in sedimentary rock.

the weather form a placer deposit as stream tin. Tinstone, tin oxide (SnO_2), is black or brown or somewhat lighter in colour, and its streak has similar hues; it has a brilliant lustre. It crystallizes in the tetragonal system, forming four-sided prisms terminated by similar pyramids, or knee-shaped twins. It is very hard and heavy (H 6 to 7; SG 7). Wood tin has a fibrous structure and forms rounded masses and those in toad's eye tin are similar but smaller. Tin mining was once a leading industry in Cornwall but it is now carried out there only on a small scale and the metal is obtained in greater quantities from Malaysia, Indonesia and also from Tasmania.

The ancients knew of lead but they seem to have regarded it as a dull utilitarian sort of metal, interesting only because of its practical use and fittingly relegated to the dim, slow-moving planet Saturn, a symbol of Old Father Time. Today it has a variety of uses, for lead piping and sheeting, in cable sheathing, for bullets and lead foil, and it forms many alloys including pewter and solder and forms the basis of white lead and red lead. As an end product in the radioactive disintegration of the element uranium, lead affords a valuable indication of the age of many of the rocks.

Of its many ores the most important is galena, lead sulphide

Cubic crystals of galena, lead ore, also called lead glance and blue lead. Its colour is lead-grey and it is very soft.

(PbS), called lead glance and blue lead, which is also a source of silver. It resembles lead in its grey colour and streak, as well as in its softness and weight (H $2\frac{1}{2}$; SG $7\frac{1}{2}$). It crystallizes in the cubic system, forming cubes or combinations of the cube and the octahedron which easily crumble into tiny cubes, or it may be massive or in grains, soft but very heavy. It used to be mined in Britain but is now chiefly obtained from the Leadville region of Colorado, the Mississippi Valley and New Mexico, USA, and from Broken Hill in New South Wales, Australia.

However mercury was discovered it must have attracted special attention as being the only metal then known which is liquid at ordinary temperatures. It seemed appropriate to assign it to the planet of the same name, emblem of the Messenger of the Gods, which although bright is so elusive, seeming to slip from side to side of the sun. Mercury has a multitude of uses in the electrical industry, in scientific, medical and domestic instruments and in the manufacture of materials ranging from explosives (fulminates) to drugs.

Almost its only source in cinnabar, mercury sulphide (HgS), with colours ranging through various shades of red and a scarlet streak. It belongs to the hexagonal system and crystallizes in

77

A large nugget of native gold. The dream of the gold prospector is a mass of gold such as this Welcome Nugget.

tabular prisms and shows good cleavage; it is soft but very heavy (H 2 to $2\frac{1}{2}$; SG 8). It comes chiefly from Spain and also from Italy and the western states of the United States.

Native gold (Au) is yellow or less often copper- or bronze-coloured, or if mixed with silver it is almost white. It has a metallic lustre and is opaque but when thin sheets of gold leaf are looked through they appear green. It crystallizes, although very infrequently, in the cubic system; it is soft enough to be cut with a knife and it is very heavy (H $2\frac{1}{2}$ to 3; SG 12 to 20), its weight varying according to the metals with which it is alloyed.

Silver occurs native, usually associated with gold, copper or other metals and also in argentite and other ores; like gold it is obtained by the amalgamation or cyanide methods. Silver (Ag) belongs to the cubic system but its crystals are usually distorted into wiry or tree-like forms and it also occurs massive. It is soft and can be flattened or worked easily but it is very heavy (H $2\frac{1}{2}$ to 3; SG 10 to 11).

Silver glance or argentite, silver sulphide (Ag_2S), is dark lead-grey, as is its streak, and it has a metallic lustre. It too belongs to the cubic system, although its crystals are often distorted, and it is soft and quite hard (H 2 to $2\frac{1}{2}$; SG over 7).

As other metals were discovered or identified there were no further heavenly bodies with which they could be associated and such a correspondence became a mere poetic fiction. Antimony, at first confused with tin, was recognized by the time of Agricola as an independent metal and the alchemists, the forerunners of modern chemists, had a special symbol for it. Its extraction from the ore is somewhat complicated and when refined it is called star antimony because of the fern-like surface markings developed during the process. At one stage it is called regulus of antimony, a term suggestive of the old days of alchemy. It has several industrial uses: in the alloy as type metal, for example, because it makes this expand as it solidifies, giving the type a clear outline.

A characteristic mass of radiating crystals of stibnite or antimony glance.

Malachite is one of the beautiful ores of copper. These photographs illustrate its nubbly surface and the concentric arrangement of its structure.

Smithsonite, a carbonate of zinc, formerly known in Britain as calamine, a term once used in the United States for hemimorphite.

The only common ore of antimony is stibnite or antimony glance, antimony sulphide (Sb_2S_3). This is also known as grey antimony because of its colour and streak; it has a metallic lustre and tarnish may make its surface iridescent. It belongs to the orthorhombic system and forms clusters of long four-sided prisms, striated lengthwise; it is soft but heavy (H 2; SG $4\frac{1}{2}$).

Zinc occurs with lead and copper and it must have been known in very early days although it does not seem to have been recognized. It may have been regarded as a sort of lead and the alloy it produced with copper, brass, may similarly have been regarded as a form of bronze (this may have been the rather mysterious orichalcum or mountain gold, said to have perished with ancient Atlantis), and perhaps as an acceptable substitute for gold. Zinc is now used not only in brass but in other alloys such as German silver and white metal, for galvanizing iron, in pigments and for other industrial purposes. Zinc, of course, is now well known as a metal but some of the early confusion still clings to the names of certain of its ores.

Zinc blende or sphalerite, zinc sulphide (ZnS), sometimes known as black jack, is commonly found with galena and the two may be difficult to separate. It is black, brown or yellow with a white or brownish streak and it may have a bright lustre. It crystallizes in the cubic system, in tetrahedra (pyramids with four triangular faces) which may be twinned; it is harder than galena but not so heavy (H $3\frac{1}{2}$ to 4; SG 4), and is brittle.

Another ore of zinc, smithsonite, zinc carbonate ($ZnCO_3$), was formerly known in Britain as calamine. It is white or off-white with a suggestion of grey, green or brown and its streak may have similar shades; it may have a glassy crust but is usually dull. Although smithsonite belongs to the hexagonal system its crystals are rare and it is usually found massive or in nubbly or kidney-shaped lumps; it is hard and of medium weight (H $5\frac{1}{2}$; SG 4 to $4\frac{1}{2}$).

Other metals were soon discovered but as mining engineers were jealous of their trade secrets and alchemists were loath to exchange ideas, it is difficult to be certain what they were. A metal spoken of rather vaguely during the Middle Ages as marcasite, and perhaps confused with zinc and antimony, may have been bismuth which was known to Agricola. This comparatively rare element produces a number of alloys, referred to as fusible metal which can be so prepared as to melt at any desired temperature, and is therefore used as a safety plug in boilers.

Bismuth glance, bismuth sulphide (Bi_2S_3), is associated with copper and other ores. It resembles lead in its grey colour but may be tarnished and it has a metallic lustre. Belonging to the orthorhombic system, it may form small needles but it is usually massive; it is soft but very heavy (H 2; SG $6\frac{1}{2}$). In Britain it is found in Cornwall and Cumberland but it occurs in greater quantities in Saxony and Bolivia.

During the eighteenth century the German mineralogists headed by Werner discovered a dozen or so new minerals, which have since developed industrial importance, notably for toughening steel, although they were not of much significance in those days. Manganese, for example, found in 1774, produces such alloys as ferro-manganese and silico-manganese; it is also used in the commercial production of oxygen, chlorine and bromine.

Among its ores is pyrolusite, manganese dioxide (MnO_2), which has a steely or iron colour with a dark brown streak and a metallic lustre. It crystallizes in the orthorhombic system but is more likely to adopt the forms of other mineral crystals, and it may be massive, fibrous or kidney shaped. It is soft enough to soil the fingers and is rather heavy (H 2 to $2\frac{1}{2}$; SG 5).

Some manganese deposits were formed under water by the action of innumerable tiny plants, like the bog manganese of the United States, Sweden and Spain. They also produce the tiny fern-like growths found inside the semi-precious stones known as moss agates; in spite of their appearance these are not fossils but are purely mineral in origin.

When identified in 1751, nickel already had an evil reputation among German miners. One of its ores has a delusive resemblance to an ore of copper but it could not be smelted and could not be made to yield any copper. They therefore decided that it must be bewitched and referred to it derisively or uneasily as Old Nick's copper (kupfernickel).

The term kupfernickel has stuck but although the metal is sometimes referred to as copper nickel, it is really arsenical nickel (NiAs) or niccolite. It is a pale coppery-red but may become tarnished; its streak is brownish-black and its lustre metallic. It belongs to the hexagonal system but is usually found massive and it is hard and very heavy (H 5 to $5\frac{1}{2}$; SG $7\frac{1}{2}$). It is still worked in Germany and also in Cornwall and in Ontario. This once despised metal is now of great industrial value, notably in the intensely hard nickel-steel alloys used in armour-plating and in the construction of cars and aircraft. Another of its alloys is the so-called German silver used in kitchenware and for ornamental work, and cupro-nickel has been used in 'silver' coins.

Cobalt also acquired a sinister reputation in Germany, being named after *Kobold*, the goblin supposed to haunt German mine workings. There seems a grim appropriateness in its possible use in the cobalt bomb, more deadly even than the hydrogen bomb and reputed to be able to sterilize large areas of ground for long periods

Cobaltite, one of the ores of cobalt. Its colour is white with a reddish tinge and its crystals have the form known as pyritohedrons.

by liberating volumes of vaporized radioactive cobalt. Cobalt is used in the production of rustproof steel and of such pigments as cobalt-blue.

Among its ores is smaltite or tin white cobalt, cobalt arsenide ($CoAs_2$), which usually contains nickel and iron. This may resemble tin or steel in its colour and metallic lustre and it has a greyish streak. It belongs to the cubic system and may produce cubes or eight- or twelve-sided crystals; it is hard and very heavy (H $5\frac{1}{2}$ to 6; SG $6\frac{1}{2}$). Smaltite is mined in Cornwall and Germany but is chiefly obtained from Cobalt, Ontario. Its presence in a rock may be indicated by a surface coating of cobalt bloom, which is not however blue but pinkish.

The bad reputation of another mineral is not a mere matter of legends but is only too well deserved, for all the compounds of the semi-metal arsenic, which in some respects acts like a metal and in others like a non-metal, are extremely poisonous. Fortunately it is not difficult to identify in the laboratory and even in the field there is a simple test for one of its principal ores: when struck with steel it emits sparks followed by a smell of garlic.

This ore is mispickel or arsenical pyrites, iron sulpharsenide (FeAsS). It is the colour of tin or steel but tarnishes pale red on exposure; it has a dark grey streak and a metallic lustre. It is orthorhombic, forming four-sided prisms ending in faces marked with striations; it is hard and very heavy (H $5\frac{1}{2}$ to 6; SG 6). In England it occurs in Devon and Cornwall, and it is also found in Saxony, in Leadville, Colorado, and in Ontario.

Tungsten is another metal that has proved useful in producing special steels for cutting tools; these steels are very strong and hard and have a high melting point. Tungsten is also used in other alloys, with chromium and aluminium, for example, and in the manufacture of electrical filaments.

Its principal ore is wolfram, an oxide of tungsten and iron or manganese ($(Mn,Fe)WO_4$). The proportion of the two metals can vary so that it forms hubnerite at one extreme and ferberite at the other, tungstates of manganese and iron respectively ($MnWO_4$ and $FeWO_4$). Its colour is chocolate brown with a similar streak and its lustre varies from dull to brilliant. It belongs to the monoclinic system and forms tabular crystals with perfect cleavage and is hard and very heavy (H 5 to $5\frac{1}{2}$; SG 7 to 8). It occurs, along with tinstone and quartz, around such granite masses as those of Cornwall and in Bolivia and Malaysia and as a placer deposit of tin and wolfram in lower Burma.

Platinum, which ranks almost as a precious metal, has an unusual history. After the discovery of South America it was first found in the Darien gold mines and its great weight, which exceeds that of gold, must have at once attracted attention. It has important uses in the electrical and other industries and it is also used in the manufacture of laboratory crucibles: it is now chiefly obtained from the United States, Canada and South Africa.

Apart from native platinum, the chief ore is sperrylite, platinum arsenide ($PtAs_2$). This is tin-white although its streak is black and it has a metallic lustre. It belongs to the cubic system and may form tiny cubes, or larger combinations of the cube and the octahedron; it is hard and very heavy (H 6 to 7; SG $10\frac{1}{2}$).

Uranium seems so severely modern that it comes almost as a shock to find that it was included by Werner in a list of metallic minerals in 1817. Some years earlier another German chemist had realized that the ore pitchblende must contain some unknown metal and had called it uranium in honour of the newly discovered planet Uranus; it was isolated later. In 1896 Becquerel noticed that pitchblende emitted rays which inexplicably fogged photographic plates and two years later the Curies discovered that it contained not only uranium but minute traces of an unknown element, radium. The significance of these facts was not realized, however, until 1945 when the first atomic bombs were dropped on Japan. Apart from its possibilities in harnessing radioactivity the uses of uranium are limited. Its chief value is in its production of radium which is used in certain types of X-ray apparatus in such medical projects as the treatment of cancer, and in the production of luminous paint.

Pitchblende or uraninite (UO_2), contains lead and other metals and various inert gases; it gets its name from its black colour and streak and from its dull pitch-like appearance. It crystallizes in the cubic system but is usually massive, granular or nubbly; it is hard

and very heavy (H $5\frac{1}{2}$; SG $6\frac{1}{2}$ to $9\frac{1}{2}$). It can be recognized by its radioactivity, which makes it affect a geiger counter and fogs photographic plates. It is found in Cornwall and in larger quantities in Central Europe, in the Congo, and near the Great Bear Lake, Canada.

Chromium forms an alloy with steel making this very hard and tenacious; chromium-plated steel is both useful and ornamental being used, for example, on motor cars and on household articles. Its chief ore, chrome iron ore or chromite ($FeCr_2O_4$), is black perhaps with shades of brown and has a brown streak and rather a faint lustre. It belongs to the cubic system and sometimes forms eight-sided crystals but is more often compact or granular; it is hard and rather heavy (H $5\frac{1}{2}$; SG $4\frac{1}{2}$ to 5). It is found in Rhodesia and large deposits occur in the central Urals of Russia.

Aluminium, aluminum in America, was not discovered until 1807 although it is one of the most abundant elements in the Earth's crust, occurring in the many silicate minerals including the feldspars and micas. Its very low specific gravity makes it of great importance whenever lightness is essential, in the aviation and

Chromite, chrome iron ore, an oxide of iron and chromium.

An early print of the Botallack tin mine on the coast of Cornwall, England. Its workings extended for over 2,000 feet under the sea.

engineering industries, for example, and it also forms some useful alloys. The intense heat generated by finely powdered aluminium is used in steel welding and in producing metals from their oxides.

Corundum, aluminium oxide (Al_2O_3), is surpassed only by the diamond in hardness. It may be grey, tinted red or green or colourless, and its lustre varies, but when more brightly coloured it produces several precious and semi-precious stones, notably ruby and sapphire. It belongs to the hexagonal system and produces barrel-shaped and pyramidal crystals which soon become waterworn or have their edges rounded; it is of medium weight and is excelled in hardness only by the diamond (H 9; SG 4). It occurs in many regions including the Transvaal.

Bauxite is an hydrated aluminium oxide ($Al_2O_3 . 2H_2O$), so mingled with impurities that its independent existence has been questioned. It is grey, brown, yellow or red, or dirty white, and is devoid of crystalline structure: its hardness varies and it is quite light (H 1 to 3; SG $2\frac{1}{2}$). It is mostly formed by the weathering of rocks containing aluminium, which are plentiful almost everywhere, but is named after the Baux region of France.

85

Non-metallic minerals

This title is not literally accurate for many of these minerals do contain metals – aluminium, magnesium and even iron – but it is an accepted expression for minerals which cannot be regarded as ores. They do not look or feel metallic, almost all are light in weight and some of them are not so much mined for as quarried. At one time they might have been described as the earthy minerals, but the term has now almost dropped out of use.

The non-metallic minerals include what are called the rock-forming minerals, those which, apart from the ores, build the greater part of the Earth's crust, and some semi-precious stones. Already they have been treated as rocks, here they are considered as the minerals which form those rocks. There are a bewildering number of them blending into one another and only those which are of special interest or importance can be mentioned.

Calcite, calcium carbonate ($CaCO_3$), is certainly a rock-forming mineral for it constitutes the bulk of the limestones and the chalk. When completely pure it is white or colourless, although it may be stained yellow, brown, red or dark grey by other minerals. Its streak too is white and it may have a glassy lustre and be almost completely transparent. It is soft enough to be scratched with a knife and is not very heavy (H 3; SG 2½). Calcite is distinguishable

Iceland spar, a transparent form of calcite, has the property of double refraction and splits an incident ray of light into two differently refracting rays.

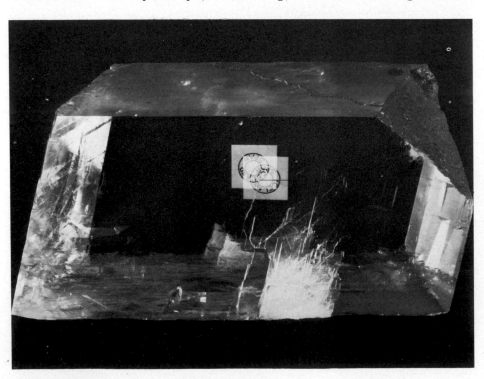

Calcite crystals with flattened tops are known as nail-head spar. Unlike quartz they effervesce in weak hydrochloric acid.

from the superficially similar mineral quartz by the bubbles of carbon dioxide it produces with effervescence when touched by weak hydrochloric acid, and is conspicuous for its perfect cleavage and its crystalline structure. It belongs to the hexagonal system and cleaves or breaks up into tiny rhombohedra each with six similar diamond-shaped faces like cubes pushed askew. The actual crystals, however, are six-sided prisms either ending in six-sided pyramids as in the variety dog-tooth spar, or with flattened tops as in nail-head spar, or in twins of various types.

Iceland spar is a very pure type of calcite, quite transparent with the very useful quality of double refraction, so that it splits light that passes through it into two slightly divergent rays; this enables it to be used in the petrological microscope.

Calcite dissolves in rain water which is a weak solution of carbonic acid and it comes out of solution again when the rain water evaporates. Deposited around mineral springs and on anything exposed to the water, it forms a crust of calcareous tufa or travertine. On the walls of caverns it forms dripstone, which hangs from the roofs of caves in stalactites and rises from their floor as stalagmites.

Aragonite resembles calcite in composition although it may contain some impurity like strontium carbonate. It too may be white,

87

Calcite deposited from running water forms growths resembling stalactites found in caves. This formation occurs in Turkey.

grey or some other colour and it may also have a glassy lustre and be transparent. It belongs to the orthorhombic system, however, and forms pointed crystals or twins which seem to be six-sided; it is slightly harder and heavier than calcite (H $3\frac{1}{2}$ to 4; SG 3). Aragonite produces a coral-like form of stalactite called flos ferri.

Dolomite or pearl spar is a double carbonate of calcium and magnesium ($CaMg(CO_3)_2$). It may be more brightly coloured than calcite and is about as hard and heavy as aragonite. It belongs to the hexagonal system and forms rhombohedra like calcite except that they may have curved faces.

Gypsum is hydrated calcium sulphate ($CaSO_4 . 2H_2O$), formed partly from the evaporation of small tracts of sea water. Commercially important in building construction it is used in the manufacture of Portland cement and plaster of paris. It may be colourless or white, perhaps tinted by iron and other impurities, and may have a glassy or silky lustre. It belongs to the monoclinic system and may produce twinned crystals of the swallowtail or arrowhead types; it is soft enough to be scratched with the fingernail and quite light (H $1\frac{1}{2}$ to 2; SG 2), and it cleaves easily into thin, somewhat flexible layers.

Crystals of gypsum are sometimes called selenite although it has nothing to do with either the element selenite or the gem moonstone – or with the moon. In its fine-grained, white form it becomes alabaster and when it is fibrous with a silky lustre, satin spar.

Apatite is thus named because of its confusing resemblance to other minerals: it is a phosphate of calcium with either fluorine or chlorine ($Ca_5F(PO_4)_3$ or $Ca_5Cl(PO_4)_3$). It is usually a pale green but may be white or grey, brown or red; it has a white streak and a glassy lustre and may be transparent. It belongs to the hexagonal system and produces six-sided prisms topped with six-sided

A large crystal of apatite, a phosphate of calcium with fluorine or chlorine, showing its hexagonal form.

pyramids which may end abruptly, and is of medium hardness and weight (H 5; SG 3). It occurs in small quantities in igneous and metamorphic rocks and in crystalline limestones.

Calcite would obviously form much more rock were it not soluble in rain water, and similarly rock salt would form immense quantities of rock if it were not dissolved even by fresh water. Rock salt or halite consists mostly of common domestic salt, sodium chloride (NaCl), but it also contains a number of other minerals which give sea water its bitterness, including a certain amount of calcite, dolomite and gypsum. When pure it is white or

A group of gypsum, calcium sulphate, crystals. Gypsum is sometimes known as selenite from its translucency and lustre.

colourless, but the other minerals may tint it; it has a glassy lustre and can be transparent or translucent. It crystallizes in the cubic system and produces cubes which may have hopper (hollow) faces; it cleaves parallel to its faces; it is soft and light (H 2 to $2\frac{1}{2}$; SG 2), and it has a characteristic taste. Rock salt occurs in many regions, notably in Cheshire in England, Saltzburg in Austria, the United States and Canada. It can either be mined in the usual way or by pumping fresh water into the rock, extracting it as brine and evaporating this.

Another mineral in some respects resembles rock salt although it is unaffected by rainfall and does not occur in sufficient quantity to be one of the rock formers. Although it is hardly a gemstone, fluorspar is valued nevertheless for its decorative possibilities. Fluorspar, calcium fluoride (CaF_2), gets its names, Derbyshire spar and Blue John respectively, from the English county where it is worked and from the French for two of its most attractive colours, *bleu-jaune*. It may also be white, colourless, amethyst or blue and it has a white streak and a glassy lustre. Like rock salt it crystallizes in the cubic system and may form cubes but it occurs in eight-sided octahedra or, of course, it may be compact; it is both harder and heavier than rock salt (H 4; SG 3). Its most distinctive feature is that it cleaves not parallel to the faces of the cubes but obliquely across their corners, parallel to the faces of the octahedron. It occurs not only in England and Europe but also in the United States.

The unusual weight of barytes, barium sulphate ($BaSO_4$), gives this mineral both its name from the Greek *barys*, heavy, and its English equivalent, heavy spar. It may be colourless or white or have other tints; its streak is white and its lustre glassy or pearly, and it may be transparent. It belongs to the orthorhombic system and forms tabular crystals. It is of medium hardness but is surprisingly heavy for a mineral which is not an ore (H 3 to $3\frac{1}{2}$; SG $4\frac{1}{2}$). Its flattish crystals may be grouped parallel to one another, forming cockscomb barytes, or in concentric layers, giving the unusual and attractive desert roses of Oklahoma, USA, a delusive resemblance to

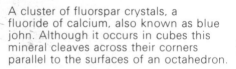

A cluster of fluorspar crystals, a fluoride of calcium, also known as blue john. Although it occurs in cubes this mineral cleaves across their corners parallel to the surfaces of an octahedron.

flowers although they consist only of mineral matter.

Of all Earth's minerals one of the most abundant, in its various forms, is quartz or silica, silicon dioxide (SiO_2). When pure it is colourless but it may be variously tinted, producing a number of precious or semi-precious stones; it may have a glassy lustre and may be quite transparent. It belongs to the hexagonal system producing six-sided prisms ending in six-sided pyramids. These might be mistaken for calcite but the quartz, although about the same weight, is much harder (H 7; SG $2\frac{1}{2}$), refusing to be scratched with a knife and, unlike calcite, it is not affected by hydrochloric acid.

Tabular crystals of barytes which may at once be recognized by its great weight as compared with that of most of the minerals which cannot be classed as ores. It is also known as heavy spar.

A cluster of quartz crystals. These may be distinguished from calcite by their great hardness and the fact that they are unaffected by acids.

Apart from its form as transparent rock crystal and from its ornamental varieties, quartz occurs in the sandstones, in many mineral veins, in such igneous rocks as granite and in some metamorphic rocks. It also forms the flints in the chalk as well as chert and hornstone.

Although quartz is the only oxide of silicon, this element has an extraordinary power of combining with itself and other minerals to produce a remarkable number of silicates; some of these are so common that they rank as rock-forming minerals. They are grouped in a score of families, some of whose members grade almost imperceptibly into one another. There are, for example, half-a-dozen micas, silicates of aluminium with potassium, sodium, lithium, magnesium or iron, forming two main groups, the muscovites and biotites.

Muscovite or white mica, the common potash mica ($KAl_3Si_3O_{10}(OH,F)_2$), was once called 'muscovy glass' because large sheets of it were formerly used in Russia as a substitute for glass. It may be white or tinted various shades and may have a pearly lustre and be transparent. Belonging to the monoclinic system, it produces what seem to be six-sided crystals; it is rather soft and light (H 2 to $2\frac{1}{2}$; SG 3). It is remarkable for its excellent cleavage, readily splitting into very thin sheets, some of them quite large; these are flexible and elastic and when held up before a strong light may show 'stars' of brightness.

Muscovite was formerly used in old-fashioned lanthorns

A crystal of mica showing its hexagonal form. The photograph opposite shows how readily it splits into thin translucent sheets.

(lanterns) and it is still used for oil-lamp 'chimneys' and for the 'windows' of oil stoves, for while it allows a fair amount of light to pass it is not cracked or otherwise damaged by heat. It is indispensable in the electrical industry as an insulator, and when powdered it has a seasonal use at Christmas to produce synthetic frost on greeting cards.

Biotite mica or black mica is a silicate of aluminium, magnesium, iron and potassium with some fluorine ($K(Mg,Fe)_3AlSi_3O_{10}(OH,F)_2$). It is not necessarily black but may be dark green when looked at but show brown or red hues, with spots or haloes of light, when thin sections are looked through; it has a bright lustre and may be transparent. It occurs in most igneous rocks. The micas not only produce these large sheets but form the glittering specks in granite and similar rocks and the bands of light-coloured material in gneiss and schist.

The chlorites resemble the micas except that they contain no alkalis, such as potassium or sodium. They occur in varied shades of green, with a pearly lustre and a slightly greasy feel. They belong to the monoclinic system and like the micas they can produce crystals which seem to be hexagonal. The flakes they form, however, are flexible but not elastic and they are soft and rather light in weight (H $1\frac{1}{2}$ to $2\frac{1}{2}$; SG $2\frac{1}{2}$ to 3).

The brittle micas are a group of hydrous magnesium silicates which rather resemble the micas except that their thin layers are brittle. Some are especially interesting. Talc ($Mg_3Si_4O_{10}(OH)_2$),

Orthoclase feldspar is a silicate of aluminium with potassium or sodium forming six-sided crystals which cleave at right-angles.

for example, may be formed by the action of intensely heated subterranean water on rocks rich in magnesium. Its colours range from silvery through various shades of green and it has a pearly lustre and may be translucent with a greasy feel. It probably belongs to the monoclinic system and is usually massive but it can split into thin layers which although flexible are not elastic. It is rather light and is remarkable for its softness (H 1; SG 3): it can be scratched with a finger nail and in its massive form, steatite or soapstone, it is easily cut with a knife and was carved into ornaments by the people of many early cultures. It also forms the tailor's French chalk.

Serpentine ($Mg_6Si_4O_{10}(OH)_8$), the mineral which forms much of the rock of the same name, is attractively variegated in colour; it may be translucent and has a slight lustre and may have a soapy feel. It belongs to the monoclinic system but it does not produce crystals, being massive or fibrous or flaky. It may be combined with steatite, which encloses fragments of serpentine after the style of a breccia. It is decidedly harder than talc (H $2\frac{1}{2}$; SG 5).

Another family of the silicates forms the feldspars, an important group of rock-forming minerals, also classed into two main groups. Orthoclase feldspar, potassium aluminium silicate ($KAlSi_3O_8$), is so called because it cleaves or splits perpendicularly. It may be white or colourless, or with shades of red or greenish-grey, with a glassy lustre and possibly transparent. It belongs to the monoclinic system and produces prismatic six-sided crystals which may be twinned, and it is hard but light in weight (H 6; SG $2\frac{1}{2}$). It is the feldspar in granite and similar rocks which gives them their colour.

The plagioclase feldspars, on the other hand, cleave or split askew; they are soda lime feldspars and grade imperceptibly from albite ($NaAlSi_3O_8$) to anorthite ($CaAl_2Si_2O_8$). They belong to the triclinic system and have several different methods of twinning; lamellar twinning, for example, is repeated so often that it forms a series of very fine layers which marks the faces of a crystal with fine parallel lines.

The colours of these feldspars range from white or grey or colourless to varying shades of pink, green or blue and some of these minerals are ornamental. Moonstone has a bluish sheen, amazonstone is bright green and labradorite may have an iridescent play of colours in which blue and green predominate.

Akin to the feldspars are the felspathoids and among these is another semi-precious stone. Lapis lazuli or lazurite, a sodium aluminium silicate with sodium sulphide, is a light blue, with a glassy lustre and may be translucent. It belongs to the cubic system but its crystals are rare and it is usually massive. In spite of its softness and lightness (H $5\frac{1}{2}$; SG $2\frac{1}{2}$) it was valued in ancient Egypt for making amulets and, when powdered, it was formerly used to produce the pigment ultramarine blue, which is now made artificially.

The olivine family of iron-magnesium silicates grades from forsterite (Mg_2SiO_4) to fayalite (Fe_2SiO_4). Olivine itself ((Mg, Fe)$_2$ SiO_4), is intermediate between them. It is a green mineral, with a colourless streak and a glassy lustre and may be transparent. Belonging to the orthorhombic system, it forms four-sided prisms ending in pyramids or rounded domes; it is of medium weight and hardness (H 6 to 7; SG 3 to 4). Fayalite is found in the Mourne Mountains in Ireland.

The pyroxene family of silicates includes augite which mostly contains calcium, magnesium iron and aluminium (($Ca, Mg, Fe,$ Al)$_2Si_2O_6$). This mineral is green to black with a glassy lustre and opaque. It belongs to the monoclinic system and forms prismatic crystals whose sides are not quite at right-angles; it is hard and rather light (H 5 to 6; SG 3 to $3\frac{1}{2}$) and it may produce twinned crystals.

The amphiboles are another family of silicates of calcium, sodium, magnesium, iron and aluminium and possibly manganese. The most distinctive is hornblende, which is black or dark green with a glassy lustre and may be translucent. It belongs to the monoclinic system and may form six-sided crystals whose faces are not at right-angles, or produce long blade-like forms; it is hard and of medium weight (H 5 to 6; SG 3 to $3\frac{1}{2}$).

One variety of amphibole was famous even in classical times. Asbestos consists of fibres long enough to be woven with a remarkable power of resisting fire, and in fact asbestos cloth could be cleansed by throwing it into flames. It is hard and light (H 5 to 6; SG 3). Also known as mountain cork or leather or wood, it is still used for producing fireproof material. It is obtained from Canada, the United States, Rhodesia and South Africa.

Asbestos has long been known because it resists the action of fire. It consists of long, fine, flexible fibres which sometimes have a silky appearance.

Although garnet crystallizes in the cubic system it has an unusual number of faces. Some of these crystals are occasionally ornamental enough to be regarded as gems.

The garnets are a family of silicates of aluminium with other metals, calcium, magnesium, iron, or manganese, or iron and calcium, or calcium and chromium. They are mostly of attractive shades of red, although some are brown or even green. They all crystallize in the cubic system, forming solid bodies with so many faces, twelve to forty-eight in number, that they resemble somewhat flattened spheres. The larger garnets are valued as gems and although of medium weight they are so very hard that smaller ones are crushed and used as abrasives, (H $6\frac{1}{2}$ to $7\frac{1}{2}$; SG $3\frac{1}{2}$ to $4\frac{1}{2}$). They are metamorphic in origin occurring in such rocks as gneiss.

The epidotes are also aluminium silicates including other metals, calcium, and perhaps also iron, manganese or cerium. They too are of metamorphic origin having been formed by the contact of molten igneous rocks with limestone. Epidote itself, a silicate of aluminium, calcium and iron, is black or green, with a glassy lustre and may be transparent. Belonging to the monoclinic system, it forms long flattish crystals; it is of medium weight but very hard (H 6 to 7; SG $3\frac{1}{2}$). A red variety, withamite, is found in Glencoe, Scotland and seems red and yellow in colour when looked through.

There are three other aluminium silicates, one of which is chiastolite (Al_2SiO_5). It is pearl-grey or reddish with a glassy lustre and perhaps with the sheen of mica on its surface. It belongs to the orthorhombic system and forms four-sided crystals, but these may be so eroded by the weather that they produce a strange shape like a rounded cross; it is very hard and of medium weight (H $7\frac{1}{2}$; SG 3 to $3\frac{1}{2}$). Chiastolite is of metamorphic origin, occurring in the slates of Cumberland and Cornwall, England.

Staurolite, another iron-aluminium silicate, perhaps also containing manganese and magnesium, is brownish-black in colour and has a grey streak; it is usually opaque but may be translucent. It belongs to the orthorhombic system but produces six-sided prisms, and it is of medium weight but hard (H 7 to $7\frac{1}{2}$; SG $3\frac{1}{2}$). It often occurs in twins, which may cross one another either askew

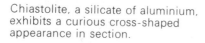

Chiastolite, a silicate of aluminium, exhibits a curious cross-shaped appearance in section.

or at right-angles, producing an almost artificial appearance; these twinned crystals may be sold as fairy crosses.

Tourmaline is a borosilicate of aluminium, perhaps also containing an alkali metal, iron or magnesium. It may be of several colours but it is usually black, and its colours may occur in concentric layers; it has a colourless streak and is usually opaque. Although tourmaline belongs to the hexagonal system, the prisms it forms are mostly triangular and it also occurs in groups of radiating needles; it is of medium weight and very hard (H 7 to $7\frac{1}{2}$; SG 3). It occurs in such rocks as granite and the metamorphic formations; the black Cornish variety is known as schorl.

A twinned crystal of staurolite, a silicate of iron and aluminium.

Almost the only form of clay which can be classed as a mineral is kaolin, china clay. This is an hydrous aluminium silicate ($Al_4Si_4O_{10}(OH)_8$) and when pure it is white but impurities may discolour it grey or buff; it has an earthy look, a greasy feel and a clayey smell. It belongs to the triclinic system but any crystals it may form crumble almost at a touch; it is very soft and quite light (H 2 to $2\frac{1}{2}$; SG $2\frac{1}{2}$). It is formed by the disintegration of the feldspar in granite.

Fuller's earth is somewhat akin to clay; it is bluish, buff or grey and crumbles easily and it has a soapy feel. It owes its name to its former use for cleaning (fulling) cloth by removing its grease and oil, and it is now used for refining oils and fats. It occurs in the sedimentary beds of south-eastern England, in Germany and in the south east of the United States.

Two mineral elements (substances which cannot be divided into anything more simple by chemical means), occur native in quantities great enough to be important in industry. One of these, native carbon, has two widely contrasting forms, the difference being due to the disparity between their atomic structures. One form, the diamond, will be discussed in the following chapter among the other gemstones.

Graphite, plumbago or black lead, (C), is black or dark grey with a black shining streak; it not only has a metallic lustre but it also feels as cold as metal. It belongs to the hexagonal system, but it mostly occurs not in crystals but in scales, cleaving parallel to their surface, or in larger masses; it is very soft and light (H 1 to 2; SG 2). Graphite has a variety of uses, both industrial and domestic; the best type comes from Siberia, and it is also found in Ceylon, the United States and elsewhere.

Sulphur, (S), like its streak, is vivid yellow and its lustre is resinous. It belongs to the orthorhombic system forming prismatic crystals bounded by pyramids, and it may also be massive or produce a crust on other rocks. It occurs in the craters and cracks of extinct volcanoes and it also forms a capping to some of the salt domes, but here again it is of volcanic origin. Sulphur is worked in the United States and elsewhere by forcing superheated water down into the deposits, to take advantage of its very low melting point (about 120° centigrade), and then driving the molten sulphur up with compressed air. It is used in the manufacture of sulphuric acid, gunpowder and fireworks, in bleaching and in vulcanizing rubber.

From descriptions such as these, it may seem almost impossible to distinguish any of the non-metallic minerals. In practice, however, each will be found to have its own individuality although this is not to be discovered from verbal descriptions, or from illustration or even from museum exhibits, but from the actual handling and study of as many mineral specimens as are available.

Opposite above A desert rose
consisting of a cluster of crystals of
barytes. Such unusual arrangements of
crystals are found in the sands of
Oklahoma, USA.

Opposite Crystals of fluorite (fluorspar).
Their purple colour is only one of the
attractive hues found in this mineral.

Above A fine hexagonal crystal of
rubellite, a variety of tourmaline,
from California, USA. The milky white
crystal is quartz.

Gemstones

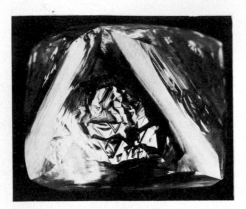

A diamond crystal in its natural state showing well-etched facets.

Washing gear used in 1888 in placer mining for diamonds in the South African workings.

Although the gemstones are non-metallic they are valued, like the precious metals, not for their use but for their appearance and rarity. Here precedence must be given to the diamond, for although it may not always be the most valuable of jewels, it is usually regarded as the most desirable, its main asset being its great hardness.

The exact nature of the diamond was long debated and it was not until the beginning of the nineteenth century that it was shown in the laboratory to consist entirely of carbon (C). It is most valued when it is colourless and transparent (of the first water), but it may also be tinted red, yellow or green – blue and black diamonds are uncommon – and translucent; it has its own characteristic adamantine lustre. It belongs to the cubic system, producing eight-sided or more seldom twelve-sided crystals; it cleaves parallel to the octahedron. It is of medium weight and is intensely hard (H 10; SG $3\frac{1}{2}$), probably the hardest substance in nature. In spite of this, however, it is rather brittle and breaks with a conchoidal fracture.

Resistant as it is, even the diamond can be water worn in the course of time by being jostled about among the pebbles of a river or on a wave-swept beach. Such a rough diamond may still attract attention by its glitter, although its true nature may not be realized, and it may, as has actually happened, become an object of passing interest only, as for example, a card player's counter or a child's plaything.

The Big Hole at Kimberley, South
Africa, is the largest man-made crater
in the world; it is more than 1,500 feet
across and 3,500 feet deep.
Millions of diamonds were extracted
from the blue ground of the volcanic
pipe by individual diggers working on
the surface. Diamonds are now mined
from the pipes by underground methods.

Diamonds traditionally come from a region in India around
Golconda, a city in Hyderabad which formed a market for gemstones. Although no actual mining was carried out at that city, its
name became synonymous with a rich source of wealth. The
modern diamond production of India is, however, not great and
new sources of supply have been discovered.

In the eighteenth century the natives of a district in Brazil were
seen using bright shiny pebbles as counters in a card game. Their
nature was soon recognized and although these diamonds were at
one time regarded, rather unreasonably, as inferior to the Indian
gems, the black Carbonado diamonds of Brazil are of great value
industrially.

In 1866 a visitor to a South African farm saw an unusual stone
lying on the floor, and asked if he could buy it. It was, he was
assured, only a child's toy picked up in the fields, and he was welcome to it. His interest in the stone was later rewarded when a
mineralogist pronounced it to be a diamond worth a considerable
sum of money. The discovery in the same region of a stone which
later became famous as the Star of South Africa stimulated a diamond rush as hectic as a gold rush. Prospecting spread from the

Overleaf A cluster of crystals of
amethyst, the purple variety of quartz,
coated with small quartz crystals.

river diggings on the Vaal to dry diggings nearby, and as many of the miners excavated their pits more and more deeply, it was only to be expected that their sides should occasionally collapse, causing serious or fatal accidents.

Eventually a diamond trust, headed by the British empire builder Cecil Rhodes, bought up the titles of the individual miners, and the diamond fields of the region are now controlled by the Diamond Corporation Ltd. which also buys rough stones from elsewhere. The Corporation moreover ensures that the market is not spoiled by being inundated with diamonds.

In this region of South Africa the diamonds are found in pipes which are associated with the craters of former volcanoes; the igneous breccia which once filled them is now cemented into a solid mass of rock called kimberlite. Its upper layers have been weathered into a loose material known as the yellow ground but

Diamonds are separated from the earthly material in which they are found by vibrating tables smeared with a layer of grease. When the grease is scraped from the tables the diamonds are found embedded in it.

Sorting the diamonds for their transparency, size and fire in the office of the diamond mines at Kimberley, South Africa.

from this all the gems have now been removed. Below this is the famous blue ground in which the diamonds still occur and further weathering would be required before these could be extracted by hand. Deeper still are harder rocks which do not contain enough of the gems to be worth working.

The shafts are actually sunk not into the blue ground where the diamonds occur but into the rocks at its side, and from these it is reached by means of horizontal galleries. The usual precautions against subsidence have to be taken, and the miners have to be supplied with air. When the rock has been loosened by drilling and blasting, it is loaded into trucks and raised to the surface in lifts. The process of weathering is then accelerated artificially. The blue ground is crushed and screened until it has been reduced to lumps of a convenient size, and then it is washed and separated from the loose sand in rotary washing pans. It is then fed on to grease tables, vibrating sheets of perforated metal covered with a layer of petroleum jelly; the diamonds adhere to this while the rest of the material passes on unaffected.

After the tables have been scraped clean and the diamonds washed loose by boiling water they are taken under a watchful guard to the mine offices, where they are sorted for sale. The whole process would be prohibitively expensive were it not for the high prices which diamonds fetch, for large quantities of the blue ground have to be excavated to produce one sizeable gem.

The rough diamond has to be subjected to a complicated process of cutting before it is suitable for sale. First its surface is marked to show the exact manner in which it must be cut so as to remove any flaws and to take full advantage of its possibilities. It is then split use being made of its natural cleavage, and further cutting is done by holding it in an implement called a dop against a revolving metal

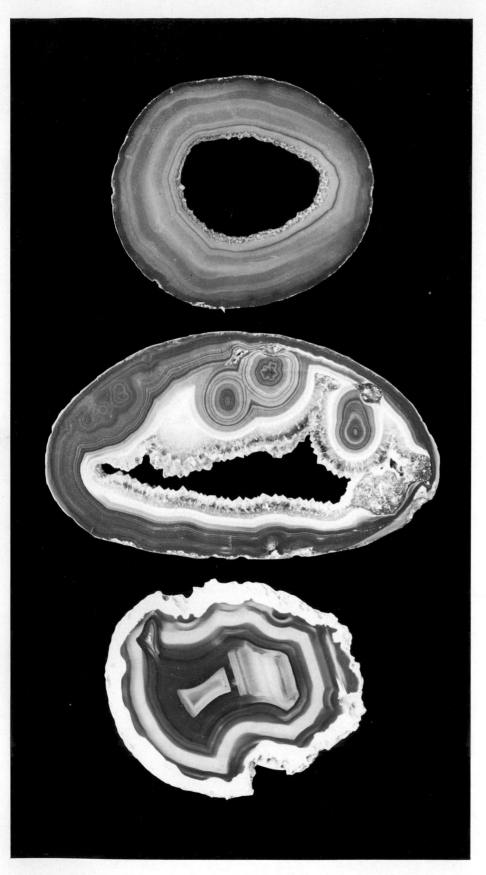

Polished sections of agate, a coloured
variety of quartz. The colours occur in
concentric layers and the cavity in the
middle of the larger stone is lined with
crystals of amethyst.

Opposite A variety of cut and polished
mineral crystals which are highly valued
as gemstones.

fluorite   zircon   tourmaline   tourmaline   garnet

garnet   phenakite   zircon   sphene

garnet   corundum   olivine   quartz   beryl

spodumene   beryl   quartz   chrysoberyl   zircon

zircon   sphalerite   tourmaline   apatite

amblygonite   spinel   scapolite   andalusite   zircon

fluorite   chrysoberyl   sillimanite   tourmaline   zircon

saw charged with a mixture of grease and diamond dust. Another tool with a diamond point rounds off its edges, and then the gem is polished to give it its facets. Here again it is held in a dop against a wheel coated with a mixture of diamond dust and oil, the only material hard enough to cut a diamond.

The brilliance of a properly cut diamond depends upon its power of refracting (bending) and internally reflecting light. Falling on to its upper surface, a ray of light is refracted so that it is twice reflected within the diamond and is then again refracted back to the observer at a somewhat different angle. It is at the same time dispersed, with hardly any reduction of its brightness, the white light being split into the colours of the rainbow thus endowing the diamond with its sparkle and fire.

Several different cuts of diamond have been devised so that each individual stone can be given the greatest possible brilliance. From merely removing odd blemishes the cutters learned as early as the fifteenth century that much was gained by giving the diamond a number of symmetrical facets. The rose cut flattens its base, above which its upper surface becomes a faceted pyramid of two tiers. A double rose might be described as two pyramids base to base, and smaller diamonds, called chips by the jeweller, may be given a few triangular facets. The double rose thus follows the symmetrical shape of the uncut diamond, having four or six similar faces above and below a central edge, the girdle.

Even so, the natural shape can be improved by giving it the brilliant cut, devised late in the seventeenth century by Vincenti Peruzzi of Venice. In this the upper and lower halves of the diamond are cut differently. The half above the girdle is given a horizontal table surrounded by thirty-two small facets and the lower half has its central point removed and replaced by a smaller collet in the midst of twenty-four larger facets. The exact size and angles of the facets are calculated in relation to the optical peculiarities of the stone.

Further modifications have since been added among them the multi-facet cut with extra surfaces and the princess cut in which the light is reflected by polished grooves. Other shapes may also be adopted but in general they do not allow the full fire of the diamond to be displayed.

Some Indian diamonds are so exceptionally large or fine that they have obtained almost world-wide renown, and as Queen Victoria was Empress of India it was only to be expected that they should become part of the royal regalia of Britain. Among these is the Koh-i-noor, the Mountain of Light, which weighs over 100 carats (a carat is approximately one-fifth of a gram; 150 carats are equivalent to an ounce); it was presented to Queen Victoria after the annexation of the Punjab in 1850. The Koh-i-noor somewhat lacks fire, however, because it is a spread brilliant, its breadth being somewhat large in proportion to its depth.

The largest known diamond was the Cullinan, found near Pretoria in 1905. This originally weighed over 3,000 carats (about one and one-third pounds), until it was cut into nine large brilliant-cut stones and nearly one hundred smaller ones. The largest of these stones, the Great Star of Africa, was given to King Edward VII by the Transvaal government; still the largest cut stone in existence, it is mounted in the sovereign's sceptre as part of the British Crown Jewels. The next largest stone is mounted in the Imperial State Crown.

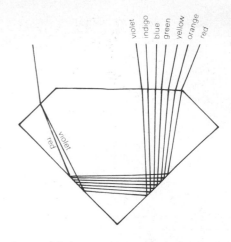

A ray of light entering a diamond crystal is refracted, reflected twice and then refracted again on leaving the crystal. Within the diamond it is split into the colours of the spectrum giving it its brilliance and fire.

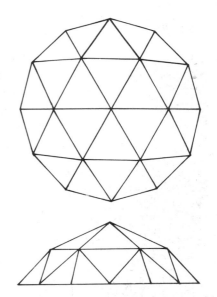

Drawings to show the top view and side elevation of the rose cut.

Opposite To polish a diamond it is held against a revolving metal plate covered with a mixture of grease and diamond dust, the only material with which a diamond can be shaped.

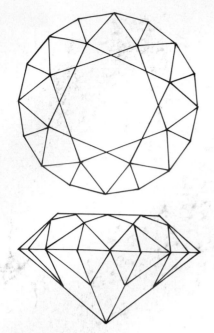

Drawings to show the top view and side elevation of the brilliant cut.

One of the most famous diamonds in the world, the Koh-i-noor, the Mountain of Light.

Opposite above A fly in amber trapped when this flowed from a tree in the form of a resin during the Cainozoic Era. Its body is preserved in every detail.

Opposite Attractive gemstones can be produced at home by tumble polishing in small machines.

The largest South American diamond, reputed to be the third largest in the world, is the Vargas, named after the president of Brazil. It weighed 727 carats before it was cut into twenty-nine stones. The largest alluvial or placer diamond was discovered in 1945 in Sierra Leone, West Africa, and weighed 770 carats. Diamonds have also been found in other regions of Africa and South America, as well as Borneo, Arkansas in the United States and New South Wales, Australia.

Lest it be thought injudicious to cut up these enormous diamonds into smaller stones, it should be remembered that other qualities are more important in a gem than mere size, notably its fire and brilliance and general attractiveness. The smaller stones may themselves be valuable individually, and the diamond dust itself is not wasted, for it can be recovered and used in cutting, shaping and polishing other diamonds.

Attempts have been made to produce synthetic diamonds by the combination of intense heat and pressure, comparable with the conditions believed to have existed in the depths of the Earth when natural diamonds were formed. Synthetic diamonds were produced in quantity only in 1954 and even then they were far too small to be regarded as gems, but in their crystalline form and their adamantine lustre they are indistinguishable from the natural stone. They are of great value industrially not only in cutting such hard minerals as corundum but in the manufacture of the diamond-tipped bits used in drilling for oil and in dressing emery wheels. The production of gem diamonds on any large scale might well lead to a great reduction in their value and have catastrophic effects on the trade in precious stones.

Diamonds have naturally acquired their own mythology, some of the stories associated with the Koh-i-noor being reminiscent of the 'Arabian Nights'. Other stones were said to have disappeared mysteriously and to have reappeared, no less mysteriously, in the gem market some years later cut to a smaller size. The disappearance of one famous diamond necklace, in which Marie Antoinette was said to have been implicated, is indeed notorious as an historical mystery which has yet to be solved.

Corundum, aluminium oxide (Al_2O_3), which has already been mentioned among the metallic minerals, constitutes a number of gemstones, the best of which vie with the diamond in value and are surpassed only by the diamond in hardness. These contrast with the common varieties of the mineral which may be colourless or a dull greenish- or reddish-grey, whereas the ruby is red and the sapphire blue. Other forms of corundum are sometimes known as the oriental amethyst, the oriental emerald and the oriental topaz, which are purple, green and yellow respectively. These terms could, however, be misleading for neither amethyst, emerald nor topaz are forms of corundum; the stones to which they refer would be better described as purple, green and yellow sapphires.

Like the other forms of corundum the ruby and sapphire belong to the hexagonal system; they produce six-sided pyramids, or double pyramids, and six-sided prisms which are so rounded as to be almost barrel-shaped, and many of them are also water worn. They are of medium weight and are very hard indeed (H 9; SG 4); they break with a conchoidal or irregular fracture.

Like the diamond, rubies and sapphires were first known in the east where they are still obtained from placer deposits, being picked out from the gravel by hand or by other methods almost as

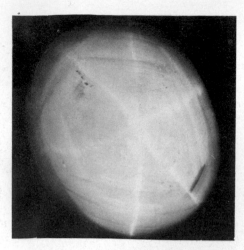

A sapphire cut en cabochon and revealing a six-rayed star which is produced by its internal crystal structure.

simple. They are especially plentiful in some regions and when the King of Burma became the owner of one of these he assumed the title Lord of the Rubies. Another district, renowned for its dark rubies, is known as the Hills of Precious Stones. In both these areas, moreover, sapphires are more plentiful than rubies. Other sources of supply are Afghanistan and Rhodesia; the stones found in Australia are dark and those of Montana, USA, are described as being a unique shade of electric blue.

The colours of the ruby are believed to be due to the presence of traces of chromium oxide, that of the sapphire to titanium. When a ruby is strongly heated it turns green, not regaining its normal colour until it has almost cooled down. If a sapphire (or less frequently a ruby) is cut en cabochon, not faceted but with a rounded top, it may become a star stone with a six-rayed star crossing its curved surface. The star appears only if the cabochon is cut in a particular way and is due to the crystal structure of the gemstone.

Another mineral containing aluminium also forms the basis of a number of gems which although not so well known are nonetheless attractive. Spinel, magnesium aluminate ($MgAl_2O_4$), may be of several colours and has a glassy lustre. It belongs to the cubic system and produces eight- or twelve-sided crystals. It is very hard, although not as hard as corundum, and is of medium weight (H 8; SG $3\frac{1}{2}$ to 4). When a clear red, it has been mistaken for ruby and what is known as the Black Prince's Ruby in the British State Crown is in fact a spinel. These red stones are called ruby spinel; rubicelle is yellow or orange; pleonaste owes its dark green colour to iron, picotite its brown colour to iron and chromium, and gahnite its dark green colour to zinc.

The element beryllium also produces gemstones which are far more widely known than spinel. Beryl, beryllium and aluminium silicate ($Be_3Al_2Si_6O_8$), is again of several colours and it has a white streak and a glassy lustre. It crystallizes in the hexagonal system and forms six-sided prisms ending in six-sided truncated pyramids; it is not quite so hard as spinel and is considerably lighter (H 8; SG 3).

The green variety of beryl is better known as emerald and was valued even in classical times both for its attractiveness and for its supposed beneficial effect on the eyes; the Emperor Nero is among those said to have used an emerald lens to relieve the strain of watching a gladiatorial show.

The Crusaders and Marco Polo are reputed to have brought emeralds from the east, but these were surpassed by those obtained from the west by the Spanish conquerors of South America. The finest of these stones, which may be as valuable as diamonds, still come from Columbia; others are obtained from the Ural Mountains of Russia and from Rhodesia and South Africa.

Aquamarine is a sea-green or bluish-green form of beryl; when yellowish-green it is sometimes distinguished by the term chrysolite aquamarine, its colour being derived from iron oxide. Most of these stones come from Brazil, others from Siberia and Madagascar and a few from the United States. Other forms of beryl are the yellow heliodor and the red or pink morganite, which is tinted by lithium.

Somewhat akin to beryl is chrysoberyl, beryllium aluminate ($BeAl_2O_4$). It is green and has a glassy lustre and may be transparent or translucent. Unlike beryl, it belongs to the orthorhombic system, but it may be twinned to produce six-sided or star-shaped

A large emerald crystal in its natural state embedded in a mass of quartz. This is a variety of beryl which crystallizes in the hexagonal system forming six-sided prisms.

forms; it is very hard and of medium weight (H $8\frac{1}{2}$; SG $3\frac{1}{2}$ to 4). Chrysoberyl is obtained from the Urals, Ceylon and Madagascar. Its greenish form alexandrite seems reddish by artificial light and another of its varieties is among the stones known as cat's eyes.

Perhaps the most important of the gem silicates is topaz, aluminium fluosilicate ($Al_2F_2SiO_4$). Its natural colour ranges from yellow to grey, blue or pink; the pink colour of some topaz, however, is produced artificially by the judicious application of heat; its streak is colourless and it has a glassy lustre. Belonging to the orthorhombic system it forms four-sided prisms, some of them tapering slightly towards their end but having a flattened top; it is very hard and of medium weight (H 8; SG $3\frac{1}{2}$). It occurs in the Urals, Brazil, Rhodesia, the Mourne Mountains of Ireland and the Cairngorms of Scotland.

The varieties of silica (quartz), silicon dioxide (SiO_2), form a number of gems and semi-precious stones, mostly distinguished by their colour. Amethyst is purple and citrine yellow; Cairngorm stones are also known as smoky quartz and morion is almost black. Rose quartz and milky quartz are described by their names and rock crystal is transparent and clear. Aventurine is a form of quartz which contains spangles of mica and other minerals, and ferruginous quartz is stained reddish or brown by iron oxides. Totally different from chrysoberyl is another type of cat's eye formed by quartz; its variants are tiger's eye, which is golden brown, and hawk's eye, which is blue.

These varieties of quartz all show their crystalline structure, but others are cryptocrystalline, their crystals being so small as to be visible only under the microscope. Some of the flints formed in chalk are hollow and are lined with purple chalcedony: these are called geodes. This mineral too has several variants; chrysoprase is apple-green, its colour being due to nickel; carnelian is red or orange and prase a dull green. Plasma and heliotrope (bloodstone) are green, flecked with white and red respectively. Jaspar is opaque, even at its thinnest, and may be brown, red or yellow.

Opal is amorphous, having no crystalline structure whatever, and its varied colours seem to alter or blend according to the angle from which it is seen. Such a play of colour, appropriately called opalescence, is especially effective in precious opal; its varieties are white, black, and fire opal.

Some forms of silica are attractively patterned. Agate is a pebble containing concentric lines of colour; onyx is banded with white and grey or brown, and sardonyx with white and pale blue and brown or red. Whereas wood opal partly consists of fossilized wood, the plant-like growths in moss agate are purely inorganic in origin, being formed of iron oxide.

Turquoise (a complicated phosphate of aluminium – its exact composition is uncertain), was familiar to the Ancient Egyptians, who mined it in the Sinai peninsula. It may be an attractive blue or green and it has a waxy lustre and is almost opaque. Although it belongs to the triclinic system, it is mostly found massive, or in kidney-like or stalactite-like formations or encrusting other rocks; it is fairly hard but rather light (H 6; SG $2\frac{1}{2}$ to 3). Bone turquoise or odontolite consists of bones or teeth stained by iron phosphate. Turquoise is easily scratched and it is porous enough to be readily damaged by detergents, soap or grease, so it is not as popular as the other gemstones.

Gems can not only be artificially shaped and worn on bracelets

A large agate in section showing very clearly the concentric arrangement of this form of quartz.

and so forth, they can also be carved into cameos, one layer of the stone being cut into while another layer of a different hue forms the background of the design. This art was developed in classical Greece, suitable gems being obtained from Egypt, and it was also favoured in classical Rome. The carving of intaglios, in which the design is hollowed out as in a seal, is even older; this method was used to make the scarabs in ancient Egypt.

A few gemstones are of organic origin. Such marine and freshwater molluscs as the mussel and the oyster line the inner surface of their shells with nacre, the mother of pearl, which is a form of calcite. As layer after layer is formed the nacre may be cut out and used in inlay work and for such articles as buttons, and it is iridescent enough to be ornamental.

If a grain of sand or other foreign body gets between the shells of the living mollusc, it sets up an irritation and to alleviate this the animal covers it with concentric layers of the nacre, forming a pearl. If it adheres to the shell it is a button pearl, but otherwise it is

Pearls are sorted and graded according to size, lustre and colour, after they have first been roughly separated in metal sieves. They are then examined individually and many are rejected because of flaws or bad colour.

almost spherical, and its size depends on the time it has taken to form.

According to some of the classical writers, pearls were at one time fairly abundant in the fresh waters of Britain. They are now chiefly formed in and near the tropical zone, in the Persian Gulf and off Ceylon and the north-western coasts of Australia. In some regions the methods used in diving for pearls are primitive, a native being equipped only with a collecting basket or net, a rope to help him back to the surface, and a knife to battle with sharks. In Australian waters, on the other hand, pearl hunters wear a diving dress.

It was the Chinese who realized, about 500 years ago, that pearls can be grown artificially by simply placing a tiny object inside the shell of a living oyster, and among the objects used were minute metal images of the Buddha. More recently the Japanese put these cultured pearls into mass production and a somewhat similar method of organizing pearl farms has now come into use

A piece of branched coral in its natural state. This occurs in some of the limestone rocks as a fossil and in the coral reefs of modern shores. It is these modern corals that are used as ornamental stones.

in Australia. There is, however, a method of distinguishing such pearls from those produced naturally.

The coral polyp is a marine creature somewhat akin to the sea anemone, the difference being that it secretes a kind of external skeleton or shell, composed of calcium carbonate, in which it lives. These shells endure after the animals that produced them have died, and if the sea level rises or the sea bed descends slowly, other coral polyps will build upon the skeletons formed by their predecessors. Thus the coral may grow, consisting either of a compact mass or of a calcite bush with numerous dividing branches, eventually becoming a coral reef. Such reefs have been formed off the coasts of Italy, southern France and North Africa, but the largest is the Great Barrier Reef off the eastern shores of Australia.

Pieces of coral are valued for their ornamental and romantic appearance. They may be white or in different shades of red, but a black coral has been obtained from the Indian Ocean and from off Hawaii, and a blue one from the West African coast.

Two gems are not of animal but of vegetable origin. Amber is a fossil resin produced during the Cainozoic Era (the Age of Mammals) by coniferous trees. Most of it is found on the Baltic coast, near Kaliningrad in Russia and Lithuania, in a material known as blue earth – totally different from the blue ground of the diamond mines. It was formerly picked up on the shore but is now systematically dredged and mined for. The Phoenician traders knew of it long ago, carrying it to the Mediterranean and using amber beads as a convenient means of exchange. It is mostly yellow or orange and occasionally white, but some specimens from Sicily and Burma are red.

An early print of a jeweller's workshop of the seventeenth century.

Amber is soft enough to be easily cut or turned and light enough to float in brine (H 2 to $2\frac{1}{2}$; SG 1). It has been worked into jewel cases, snuff-boxes, religious images, and even sets of chessmen, and is still used for pipe-stems and cigarette holders. The chief attraction of amber lies in the small insects and other oddments which it encloses; it trapped them when the resin was still liquid enough to flow sluggishly, and later hardened around them. As many of the insects are of species which existed ages ago and which are now extinct, and as they are preserved in great detail, they are of especial interest to biologists and palaeontologists.

Jet is a form of lignite (brown coal) hard enough to be polished and yet soft enough to be turned in a lathe or cut with a knife. Its funereal colour formerly made it seem appropriate for religious articles and for wear during periods of mourning, but this custom has now passed out of use. Jet was used during the Bronze Age for making ornaments.

From classical times onward the great centre for jet production has been Whitby, on the coast of Yorkshire, England; before the Reformation the monks of Whitby Abbey used it for making crosses and rosary beads. Like the Baltic amber it was formerly picked up on the shore but it is now systematically mined for. Inferior types of jet are also obtained from Spain and elsewhere.

Apart from artificial diamonds, imitation gems can now be fabricated from synthetic corundum produced from powdered aluminium oxide. If this is melted in an oxy-hydrogen blowpipe it produces a pear-shaped mass known as a boule. Without any colouring matter this forms synthetic white sapphire, but the addition of an appropriate chemical converts it into other synthetic gems, almost indistinguishable from the natural types.

Imitation or costume jewellery is, of course, very old, but here the aim is to produce not an artificial gem but something which at a distance, on the stage, for example, will look sufficiently like the real thing to pass scrutiny. For this purpose the usual material is glass, known technically but inaccurately as paste, although plastics are now being used. Both can be coloured as desired and glitter convincingly.

Apart from the actual gems, which are mostly expensive and some of which are very costly indeed, there is a wide variety of what might be called 'semi-precious stones', a term frowned on by the purists as too vague to have any meaning; 'ornamental stones' might be better. They range from brilliantly coloured ores such as malachite to non-metallic minerals like the garnets.

Collecting and identifying specimens

The collection of rocks and minerals has the advantage not only of taking its enthusiasts out into the country but of helping them to understand and enjoy it. This is as true of the 'rockhound' avid for the raw material of future gemstones as of the serious student of rocks, fossils or minerals and the influence of geology on the scenery.

The search for mineral specimens can involve strenuous outdoor activity but if ordinary precautions are taken it can hardly be regarded as hazardous. It can, however, have its perils for those not accustomed to going out into the countryside. Even small and densely populated regions claim their toll of those who have gone astray or been caught by the weather on mountains or moors, and a few cautionary words are included here to help avoid such mishaps.

When climbing or on rough ground it is essential to play for safety, to move only one limb at a time and make sure that other limbs are securely placed, and to avoid sudden movements. It is easy to slip not only on snow or ice but on a grassy or muddy slope, and apparently firm ground may end in a quagmire or a cliff.

Cliffs indeed offer a double risk and one must avoid not only their edge but also their foot, for loose rocks may fall without warning. A cliff face which at first seems very easy to scale may lead to a position from which it is impossible either to proceed further or to descend, and it should be remembered that it is no subject for a violent assault with a hammer. It goes without saying that any proposed collecting expeditions verging on mountaineering should be attempted only under experienced leadership.

The sea coast also has perils. The rising tide can trap a beach-comber at the foot of an unscaleable cliff and in the shallows it can advance with incredible speed. What seems a firm beach, furthermore, may conceal a quicksand which might well lead to a tragedy. Local enquiries should always be made as excursions are planned to obviate any such disasters.

The study and exploration of caves, speleology, is a specialized branch of geology, and caving, which has well been called mountaineering in reverse, has the total absence of daylight to complicate the perils of normal mountaineering. Here again, therefore, an experienced leader should be chosen and his instructions carefully followed during an expedition.

Old mine workings are particularly dangerous. Permission to descend mines actually in use is sometimes given to students of geology, but they must be willing to accept the very reasonable proviso that they act entirely at their own risk and cannot expect compensation for any accident. They must be careful never to obstruct the miners or interfere with the machinery and always to obey all the directions given by their guide. Leave to go over the surface workings of a mine or to visit a quarry is more readily given. Here it may be possible to pick up good specimens from the spoil heaps or to purchase them fairly cheaply from the workmen.

The actual winning of specimens has only one risk, that of using a geological hammer too vigourously. This might send chips of rock flying up dangerously near the eyes so that anyone wishing to use a five pound hammer on some obdurate stone should wear goggles.

Interest in science is no excuse for trespassing, and before private land is entered permission should be asked and it should be made clear what is involved. Probably nobody would object to the removal of odd bits of stone but a farmer, for example, would want an assurance that none would be left lying about in the open where they might injure cattle. It need hardly be mentioned that fires should not be lit without permission and that gates should always be left as they are found.

Clothing need not be too new; clambering over rocks can play havoc with a prospector's skin, so that trousers are better than shorts or a lady's skirt. A waterproof and windproof anorak is always advisable and as waiting about in exposed places may be involved, an extra pullover is desirable. Boots are preferable to shoes because of the support they give to the ankles, and an outer pair of socks turned down over the boot tops will keep out loose rock fragments or grit.

Little specialized equipment is needed for gathering rock specimens. A note book enables records to be made of where anything interesting was found and of what it is or seems to be, and unless they are made at once it is amazing how soon they will be forgotten. Sites should if possible be identified by the grid reference on large-scale maps of the area. Specimens will have to be not only carried but also protected from damage. A rucksack or haversack is suitable for carrying them and it should not be overloaded, for rocks and minerals, hardly light at best, seem to get heavier the further they are carried. A supply of small boxes or polythene bags or paper will enable each specimen to be carried separately to protect it from harm. A gummed slip of paper should be fastened to each and numbered, and an entry of its origin and nature made in the note book.

If specimens apart from pebbles from the beach are to be collected a geological hammer, with a straight haft and head squared at one end with a chisel edge at the other, will be needed for breaking off and splitting fragments of rock. For splitting hard rocks a cold chisel is helpful; two are better so that if one gets wedged in a crevice the other can be used to free it. When work in clay or sand is involved a trowel or broad-bladed knife can replace the hammer.

Specimens can be identified in the field by consideration of the characteristics of minerals discussed in chapter five but the tests mentioned will need to be somewhat simplified to obviate the need for carrying apparatus. The hardness of a mineral can be adequately described as very soft (H 1 to 2) if it can be scratched with a fingernail; soft (H 3 to 4) with the edge of a coin; medium (H 5 to $5\frac{1}{2}$) with the blade of a knife; hard (H 6 to 7); and very hard (H 8 to 10). Regarding its weight, it is enough to judge this by hefting the specimen and classing it as very light (SG 1 to 2); light ($2\frac{1}{2}$ to

3); medium (3½ to 4); heavy (4½ to 5); and very heavy (over 5).

The streak of a mineral can perhaps be ascertained by an attempt to use it to mark a sheet of paper or a piece of rock. A small acid bottle, with a glass stopper to prevent leakage, will enable a little dilute hydrochloric acid to be used for testing for calcite, which is betrayed by its effervescence on contact with the acid. The angle of dip of a rock bed, its downwards slope from the horizontal, can be estimated by eye; the direction of the dip and of its strike (its general run across country, which is always at right-angles to its dip) can be read from the compass which anyone who leaves the beaten track needs for his own guidance. A compass is also useful to test for magnetite.

If access to a laboratory is available the nature of a mineral can be ascertained with great exactitude either by the usual methods of chemical analysis or more simply by the use of a blowpipe. For details of these techniques, however, the reader is referred to the larger and more technical works on mineralogy.

The best way to learn how to identify minerals, however, is to study the specimens in museums and in private collections and, if possible, to get permission to handle them. Thus the beginner may acquire the ability of the early prospector and the experienced geologist to be able to recognize specimens with little more than a glance and a touch. Meanwhile, he may be able to learn from a museum or college, or a knowledgeable friend, what the 'hand specimens' he has collected are, whether he has named them provisionally or whether they have baffled him completely.

The term 'hand specimen', as it implies, means a piece of rock or mineral or a pebble small enough to be conveniently handled. One of each type will normally suffice, except that where a rock is much altered by weathering two may be needed, one from its unaltered interior and one from its weathered surface.

For travel on foot a one-inch to the mile map, or its metric equivalent, is ideal, but for advanced study an uncoloured six-inch map is preferable. On this the 'prospector' may lightly pencil all the relevant information he can obtain from the museum, library, or guidebooks or works on the local geology. This will include positions of the places where the rocks are actually exposed and the nature of their beds and so forth. Other exposures may be found in the field: likely places are sea cliffs and beaches, quarries and mines, cuttings for roads and disused railways, ditches, trenches dug for the walls of new buildings, the mouths of burrows – wherever in fact the soil, or better still the underlying rocks, have been made visible.

From the soil itself much is to be learned, not only from loose pieces of the underlying rocks which have come to the surface but from its own colour and consistency and from the vegetation which it supports. A few clumps of bluebells in the midst of a copse in which they are found nowhere else, for example, might suggest a patch of sand overlying a tract of clay.

When a few probable exposures have been located, a route should be worked out joining them and the expedition carefully planned. Overnight sleeping accommodation should be arranged if more than one day's work is contemplated and camping gear is not being carried, and transport back to civilization should not be forgotten. The route need not be followed too strictly if anything is gained by changing it, but in unfrequented country it may be desirable to leave word of what is proposed, in case of accident.

The direction of dip (slope) of a bed of stratified rock can be measured in the field by means of a special geological compass.

It is advisable to make first-hand notes when collecting specimens in the field and exposures of rocks can be plotted on geological maps.

The outdoor collection of rock specimens can be supplemented by study of established mineral collections. A personal collection is easy to start but each specimen should be kept in its own shallow container which can be marked with particulars of its nature and the place where it was found.

Rough stones collected from the rocks can be conveniently turned into attractive gemstones in a tumble polishing machine; the stones are smoothed and polished in a revolving cylinder containing a special grit.

Work in the field can be supplemented by fascinating indoor occupations. There are the specimens to be studied, and a handyman might be able to make suitable cabinets with shallow drawers in which they can be stored; failing this, odd boxes, even match boxes, may suffice, but the deliquescent rock salt should be kept in a tightly closed jar. The rough notes made in the open can be amplified by information gained elsewhere and written up in a field note book, which might be illustrated by sketches or photographs. This can become the technical equivalent of a diary of great specialized interest. Theoretical aspects of the science can be studied and diversified by the exercises on geological maps which are obtainable, showing how the lie of the rock beds can be deduced from surface indications. Experience in this technique can be very helpful in the field. Museum visits and if possible attendance at lectures should not be neglected. It would be still better if a student could join an evening class or a geological field club.

A fascinating type of handicraft has recently developed whereby oddments of suitable stone can be transformed into articles of jewellery which many people would be glad to own and many ladies proud to wear. Already this interest in lapidary work has produced instructional books, a small magazine and shops which provide suitable stones and technical equipment.

The most popular and useful piece of equipment is a motorized tumble polishing machine in which rough stones are smoothed by rotation in a cylinder containing a suitable grit. Smaller items include cutting and grinding wheels of different types with dop sticks for holding the stones securely against them; polishing powder; and a variety of jewellery settings – rings, brooches, ear clips, and so forth – in which the finished stones may be suitably mounted. Amateur lapidarists with a taste for outdoor activity may prefer to go out into the country to hunt for suitable stones rather than simply to purchase them from shops, and there are books as well as magazine articles giving lists of the regions where they may be found.

Experience shows that interest in geology can be as rewarding as in other branches of natural history. It is no less pleasing to be able to recognize a type of rock or a mineral, or for that matter a fossil, than a flower, a tree, a bird or animal or a cloud formation. True, the former lack the emotional appeal of the living creatures, but the build and formation of the countryside has an appeal of its own.

Books to read

On rocks and minerals:
The Mineral Kingdom by Paul E. Desoutels. Hamlyn, London, 1969. Madison Square Press, New York, 1968.
Rocks and Minerals by Herbert S. Zim and Paul R. Schaffer. Hamlyn, London, 1971.
Collecting Rocks and Fossils by J. B. Delair. Batsford, London, 1966.
The Rock Book by C. L. and M. A. Fenton. Doubleday, New York, 1940.
Minerals and Rocks in Colour by J. F. Kirkaldy. Blandford, London, 1970.
Rutley's Elements of Mineralogy by H. H. Read. Allen and Unwin, London, 1971.
Meteorites by A. A. Moss. Trustees of the British Museum (Natural History), London, 1971.

On gemstones:
Practical Gemmology by Robert Webster. N.A.G. Press, London, 1966.

For amateur gemmologists and rockhounds:
Collecting and Polishing Stones by Herbert Scarfe. Batsford, London, 1970.
The Pebbles on the Beach by Clarence Ellis. Faber, London, 1969.

For fieldwork:
Elements of Field Geology by G. W. Himus and G. S. Sweeting. University Tutorial Press, London, 1955.

Acknowledgements

Colour illustrations Ammonite Ltd. 111 bottom; Ardes Photographics 111 top; Associated Freelance Artists Ltd. 66; Barnabys Picture Library 15 bottom; Bruce Coleman Ltd. 34 bottom, 38 top; Crown copyright Geological Survey photographs reproduced by permission of the Director, Institute of Geological Sciences 43, 71 bottom, 74, 75 bottom, 102/103, 107; W. F. Davidson 35 bottom, 42 bottom, 98 bottom; Hamlyn Group Photographic Library 75 top, 79, 98 top, 99, 106; Picturepoint Ltd. 39, 67 top, 71 top; Studio Bevilacqua 15 top; ZEFA 11, 34 top, 35 top, 38 bottom, 42 top, 67 bottom.

Black and white illustrations Aerofilms Ltd. 16 bottom, 40, 52; Barnabys Picture Library title page, 12 bottom, 16 top, 17, 24, 61, 88; De Beers Consolidated Mines Ltd. 101, 109; Trustees of the British Museum (Natural History) 51 bottom, 53 left, 63, 70, 72, 78, 82, 89 top, 91 top, 92, 100 top; J. Allan Cash 10, 13, 14, 28, 49, 51 top, 104, 105, 108, 115; Crown copyright Geological Survey photographs reproduced by permission of the Director, Institute of Geological Sciences 6, 18, 19, 23, 26, 27 top, 29–33, 36, 41, 44, 45, 46, 48, 53 right, 54, 64, 69, 73, 76, 77, 84, 86, 87, 89 bottom, 90, 91 bottom, 93–97, 112, 114, 122 top; Iceland Photo and Press Service, photographed by Mats Wibe Lund Jnr. 37; John Gay 8, 9, 12 top, 21; Kernowcraft Rocks and Gems Ltd. Truro, Cornwall, suppliers of lapidary equipment 122 bottom; Larousse 27 centre, 47, 80; Mansell Collection 50, 117; Popperfoto 57; Radio Times Hulton Picture Library 7, 58–60, 84/85, 100 bottom; Shell Photographic Unit 121; United States Information Service 55.

The line drawings on pages 109 and 110 are based on originals by Robert Webster F.G.A. which appear in Practical Gemmology by Robert Webster, published by N.A.G. Press.

Index